Introduction to Chemistry

CHEM 1305

CENGAGE Learning

Australia • Brazil • Japan • Korea • Mexico • Singapore • Spain • United Kingdom • United States

Introduction to Chemistry
CHEM 1305

Executive Editor:
Michael Stranz

Managing Lab Editor:
Jeff Nunn

Custom Lab Editors:
Cooper Gouge, John Horvath

Custom Production Editor:
Jennifer Flinchpaugh

Project Coordinators:
Lisa Donahue. Peg Hagar

Senior Pre-Press Specialist:
Riley Gibb

Production Supervisor-Labs:
Melanie Evans

Rights and Permissions Specialist:
Kalina Ingham Hintz

Senior Marketing Coordinator:
Sara Mercurio

ISBN-13: 978-0-495-25780-6

ISBN-10: 0-495-25780-X

Cengage Learning
5191 Natorp Blvd.
Mason, OH 45040
USA

Cengage Learning is a leading provider of customized learning solutions with office locations around the globe, including Singapore, the United Kingdom, Australia, Mexico, Brazil, and Japan. Locate your local office at:
international.cengage.com/region

Cengage Learning products are represented in Canada by Nelson Education, Ltd.

Visit Signature Labs online at **signaturelabs.com**

Visit our corporate website at **cengage.com**

Printed in the United States of America

Acknowledgements

The content of this text has been adapted from the following product(s):

PROP 602: Determining Density
ISBN-10: (0-87540-602-5)
ISBN-13: (978-0-87540-602-2)

PROP 603: Resolving a Two-Component Mixture
ISBN-10: (0-87540-603-3)
ISBN-13: (978-0-87540-603-9)

REAC 604: Observing Signs of Chemical Reaction
ISBN-10: (0-87540-604-1)
ISBN-13: (978-0-87540-604-6)

ANAL 605: Determining the Percent Water in an Unknown Hydrate
ISBN-10: (0-87540-605-X)
ISBN-13: (978-0-87540-605-3)

STOI 606: Determining the Empirical Formula of Magnesium Oxide
ISBN-10: (0-87540-606-8)
ISBN-13: (978-0-87540-606-0)

MISC 459: Naming Inorganic Compounds
ISBN-10: (0-87540-459-6)
ISBN-13: (978-0-87540-459-2)

ANAL 620: Separating and Identifying FD&C Dyes Using Paper Chromatography
ISBN-10: (0-87540-620-3)
ISBN-13: (978-0-87540-620-6)

MISC 614: Writing, Interpreting, and Balancing Chemical Equations
ISBN-10: (0-87540-614-9)
ISBN-13: (978-0-87540-614-5)

REAC 610: Observing Single Replacement Reactions
ISBN-10: (0-87540-610-6)
ISBN-13: (978-0-87540-610-7)

MISC 490: Using Exponential Notation and Significant Figures
ISBN-10: (0-87540-490-1)
ISBN-13: (978-0-87540-490-5)

REAC 611: Observing Some Double Replacement Reactions
ISBN-10: (0-87540-611-4)

ISBN-13: (978-0-87540-611-4)

REAC 613: Classifying Some Chemical Reactions
ISBN-10: (0-87540-613-0)
ISBN-13: (978-0-87540-613-8)

ANAL 624: Identifying Cations in a Solution
ISBN-10: (0-87540-624-6)
ISBN-13: (978-0-87540-624-4)

STRC 434: Writing Lewis Symbols and Lewis Structures
ISBN-10: (0-87540-434-0)
ISBN-13: (978-0-87540-434-9)

Table Of Contents

modular · laboratory · program · in · chemistry

program editor: H. A. Neidig

Writing Lewis Symbols and Lewis Structures

prepared by **H. A. Neidig**, Lebanon Valley College and
J. N. Spencer, Franklin and Marshall College·

Purpose of the Experiment

Write Lewis symbols for elements and monatomic ions. Write Lewis structures for molecules and polyatomic ions. Write chemical equations using Lewis structures for reactions involving either ionic compounds or covalent compounds. Predict the empirical formulas of ionic compounds and covalent compounds based on the Lewis symbols for their constituent ions or atoms, and write Lewis structures for the compound.

Background Information

Chemists use models in order to better understand the nature of matter. For example, chemists can often represent the chemical structure of a substance using a physical model. Chemists study the model to learn more about the shape and relative sizes of atoms, molecules, or ions making up the substance and the spatial relationships among these components. Based on such a model, chemists can usually predict the physical and chemical behavior of the substance.

Every atomic nucleus is surrounded by at least one electron. Generally, only the **valence electrons**, or outer electrons, are chemically active. Chemists use a model called the **Lewis electron-dot symbol** to depict the valence electrons. The Lewis electron-dot symbol consists of two parts: the chemical symbol and electron dots. Lewis symbols for monatomic ions also include an indication of the charge on an ion; for example,

$$: \overset{\displaystyle ..}{\underset{\displaystyle ..}{Cl}} : ^{-}$$

Bonds hold the atoms of a substance together. We can depict the bonding in a molecule or polyatomic ion by building a model of the species. To do this, chemists use a **Lewis structure**. The Lewis structure for a species is based on the Lewis symbols for the atoms making up the species. A Lewis structure shows the different atoms in the species, the number of each kind of atom in a unit of the species, and the distribution of all valence electrons.

Writing Lewis Symbols for Atoms and Monatomic Ions

In the Lewis symbol, the chemical symbol of an element represents the nucleus and inner, non-valence, electrons of one atom of an element. We call this portion of the Lewis symbol the **atomic core.** We represent the valence electrons using dots around the atomic core.

When working with representative elements in the periodic table, we determine the number of valence

CENGAGE Learning™

electrons associated with each of these elements from its position on the periodic table, which is current American usage. The number heading each group, or column, of the table indicates the number of valence electrons for each element in that group. Lewis symbols and Lewis structures work best for elements in the first three periods, or rows, of the periodic table.

When we write Lewis symbols for elements, we will construct our model by **arbitrarily** placing the electron dots one at a time, one on each of the four sides of the atomic core. If there are more than four electrons we just keep going around the symbol, until all of the valence electrons are represented by dots.

For example, if we want to write the Lewis symbol for lithium (Li) we begin by noting that Li is in Group I in the periodic table. Therefore, it has one valence electron. Hence we use one dot to represent the single valence electron, and we write the Lewis symbol for a lithium atom as:

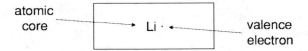

Next consider an atom of fluorine (F). Because fluorine is in Group VII of the periodic table, we know that it has seven valence electrons. As a result, two of fluorine's seven valence electrons are found on each of three sides of the atomic core of fluorine and one electron on the fourth side. Thus we write the Lewis symbol for a fluorine atom as:

$$:\ddot{\text{F}}\cdot$$

To write Lewis symbols for ions, we use the Lewis symbols for the appropriate atoms and add or subtract electrons, depending on the charge on the ion. A negative charge indicates that the ion contains more electrons than does the neutral atom. A positive charge indicates fewer electrons than the neutral atom. The negative sign in the Lewis symbol for the fluoride ion indicates that the ion has one more electron than a neutral fluorine atom has. Thus, the Lewis symbol of the fluoride ion is:

$$:\ddot{\text{F}}:^{-}$$

This symbol includes eight electron dots written as four pairs around the fluoride ion.

Consider the Lewis symbol for the lithium ion:

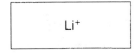

Because a lithium atom loses its single valence electron when it becomes a lithium ion, we write the Lewis symbol for a lithium ion without any valence electrons and add the plus sign to indicate the ion's positive one charge.

We write the Lewis symbol for the aluminum ion in a similar way.

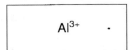

The aluminum atom loses three valence electrons when it becomes the aluminum ion, so we write the Lewis symbol for an aluminum ion without any valence electrons and add the number 3 followed by a plus sign to indicate the ion's positive three charge.

Writing Lewis Structures for Molecules and Polyatomic Ions

In chemical reactions, electrons are transferred or shared between atoms, producing ionic or covalent compounds. When electron transfer occurs, the result is the formation of positive and negative ions. A compound made up of a combination of positive and negative ions is an ionic compound. You are probably already familiar with the chemical formula NaCl that shows the ions of sodium and chlorine have bonded to form the ionic compound sodium chloride. In solid sodium chloride, each Na^+ ion is surrounded by six Cl^- ions and each Cl^- ion by six Na^+ ions. We will use the **arbitrary** designation Na^+; Cl^- to illustrate the ionic nature of the compound and the **arbitrary** designation

$$\{\ [\text{Na}]^+;\ [:\ddot{\text{C}}\text{l}:]^-\ \}$$

to illustrate the ionic nature of its Lewis structure. We call the attraction that holds oppositely charged ions together an **ionic bond.**

While a Lewis symbol can represent individual atoms or monatomic ions, a Lewis structure can represent the bonding between atoms in a molecule or polyatomic ion. In these species, pairs of electrons are shared between atoms, forming **covalent bonds.**

Consider a hydrogen molecule (H_2). Each hydrogen atom has one valence electron and its Lewis symbol is H·. The covalent bond between the two hydrogen atoms in a hydrogen molecule has a pair of electrons shared between the two bonding partners. The Lewis structure for the hydrogen molecule is:

$$H:H$$

Atoms joined by covalent bonds form **covalent compounds**. For convenience, we often represent shared electron pairs in a Lewis structure using a dash, rather than two dots.

$$H-H$$

one shared electron pair

In some molecules, atoms are joined by multiple covalent bonds. When two electron pairs are shared, such as between carbon atoms in ethylene (C_2H_4), a double bond forms. In a Lewis structure, we represent the double bond between two atoms by using two dashes rather than four dots.

two shared electron pairs between carbon atoms in ethylene

When atoms are joined by a triple bond, we represent the three shared electron pairs using three dashes rather than three pairs of dots, as shown in acetylene.

$$H-C\equiv C-H$$

three shared electron pairs between carbon atoms in acetylene

The outer electron levels of atoms of non-metallic elements usually accommodate a maximum of eight electrons each by accepting electrons from other elements. When this occurs, the resulting outer electron configuration of each atom is like that of a rare gas, such as neon (Ne) or argon (Ar). Because we call a group of eight valence electrons an **octet**, we say that this configuration is in accordance with the **octet rule**. We understand that this is only a rule and not a law. Exceptions occur, but, even with these exceptions, Lewis structures are used to give acceptable explanations.

For atoms of hydrogen and helium, a filled outer electron level contains just two electrons. When a hy-

drogen atom has two electrons, we say that this configuration is in accordance with the **duet rule**.

Let's apply the octet rule when writing the Lewis structure for the fluorine molecule (F_2), which has a single covalent bond. First, we check the periodic table and see that fluorine is in the VIIB column, indicating each fluorine atom has seven valence electrons. Then, we add the total number of valence electrons in the two fluorine atoms, which equals 14. Next, we write the two atomic cores, as shown in Figure 1(a). Then, we write two dots between the fluorine atoms, representing the shared pair of electrons making up a covalent bond, as shown in Figure 1(b). Finally, we distribute the remaining 12 valence electrons so that each fluorine atom has an octet of electrons. To do so, we represent the 12 electrons as three pairs of dots around each of the two fluorine atomic cores. Figure 1(c) shows the Lewis structure for the fluorine molecule, in which each fluorine atom has an octet.

Figure 1 *The Lewis structure for the fluorine molecule, F_2. (a)The atomic cores; (b)the electron-pair covalent bond; (c)the distribution of remaining valence electrons*

When we write the Lewis structure for a polyatomic ion, we must be sure to represent each of the valence electrons in the Lewis structure. For example, in the polyatomic hypochlorite ion (OCl^-), oxygen has six valence electrons, chlorine has seven valence electrons, and there is one additional electron that gives the ion its overall negative-one charge. Therefore, for OCl^-, the total number of valence electrons is $6 + 7 + 1 = 14$. The Lewis structure for the hypochlorite ion is therefore:

Note that in this structure both oxygen and chlorine have electron octets, thus both are in accordance with the octet rule.

Writing Chemical Equations Using Lewis Symbols and Lewis Structures

We can write chemical equations for some reactions using Lewis symbols and Lewis structures for reactants and products. For example, the chemical equation for the reaction of lithium atoms (Li) and fluorine (F_2) molecules is shown in Equation 1. The semicolon is placed in the resulting ionic compound structure to indicate a separation, but attraction, of the ions in the ionic compound. Furthermore, the resulting structure is placed inside a pair of braces to further emphasize lithium fluoride as an ionic compound.

$$2 \, Li \cdot + \, : \overset{\cdot \cdot}{\underset{\cdot \cdot}{F}} : \overset{\cdot \cdot}{\underset{\cdot \cdot}{F}} : \rightarrow 2 \, \{ \, [Li]^+; \, [: \overset{\cdot \cdot}{\underset{\cdot \cdot}{F}} :]^- \} \qquad (Eq. \, 1)$$

In this reaction the lithium atom loses an electron to a fluorine atom and becomes a lithium ion, Li^+. The fluorine atom gains an electron and becomes a fluoride ion, F^-. The product is the ionic compound lithium fluoride, LiF, for which we write Li^+; F^-. In this compound neither the lithium ion nor the fluoride ion share any valence electrons. Hence, the compound has no covalent bonds. The fluoride ion has an octet of valence electrons, like that of a rare gas, and is in accordance with the octet rule.

Similarly, we can write the chemical equation for the combustion reaction of methane (CH_4) and oxygen (O_2) using Lewis structures, as shown in Equation 2. Note that the reactants and products are all covalent compounds.

$$\underset{\overset{|}{H}}{\overset{\overset{H}{|}}{H - C - H}} + 2 \, \overset{\cdot \cdot}{\underset{\cdot \cdot}{O}} = \overset{\cdot \cdot}{\underset{\cdot \cdot}{O}} \rightarrow$$

$$\overset{\cdot \cdot}{\underset{\cdot \cdot}{O}} = C = \overset{\cdot \cdot}{\underset{\cdot \cdot}{O}} + 2 \, H - \overset{\cdot \cdot}{\underset{\cdot \cdot}{O}} - H \qquad (Eq. \, 2)$$

Predicting Empirical Formulas from Lewis Structures

We can also use Lewis structures to predict the empirical formula of a substance formed from the reaction of two elements. For example, suppose we want to write the Lewis structure of the product formed from the reaction of silicon (Si) and hydrogen (H_2). Suppose we then want to predict the empirical formula of the compound, based on its Lewis structure. Silicon is in Group IV of the periodic table, so we know that it has four valence electrons. We already know that hydrogen has one valence electron. Looking at the Lewis symbols for

silicon ($\cdot \, \overset{\cdot}{Si} \, \cdot$) and hydrogen (H $\cdot$)

we know that each silicon atom can share four additional electrons, so each silicon atom can bond to four hydrogen atoms. In the resulting structure, each silicon has an electron octet, and each hydrogen has an electron duet. Given the ratio of four hydrogen atoms bonding to each silicon atom, the empirical formula for the product must be SiH_4. The equation for this reaction, written using Lewis structures, is shown below in Equation 3.

$$\cdot \, Si \cdot + 2 \, H : H \rightarrow \underset{\overset{|}{H}}{\overset{\overset{H}{|}}{H : \overset{\cdot \cdot}{Si} : H}} \qquad (Eq. \, 3)$$

In this experiment, you will use Lewis symbols and Lewis structures as models for elements, ions, and ionic and covalent compounds. Based on Lewis symbols for selected substances, you will predict the possible products of their chemical reactions. You will write chemical equations using Lewis symbols and Lewis structures to represent reactants and products. Based on the Lewis symbols of selected elements, you will determine the possible empirical formula and Lewis structure for the products.

Procedure

For each of the following questions, write in the requested information. Refer to a periodic table while answering the questions.

I. Writing Lewis Symbols and Lewis Structures

1. Fill in the spaces in the following table with the Lewis symbols for the third period elements listed.

Na	Mg	Al	Si	P	S	Cl	Ar
	$\cdot$ Mg $\cdot$		$\cdot$ Si $\cdot$				: Ar :

2. Write the Lewis symbol for each of the following:

magnesium ion_____ argon_____ iodide ion_____

cesium ion_____ oxygen ion_____

3. Construct the Lewis structure model for the ionic compound potassium chloride using the following steps.

(1) The number of valence electrons in a potassium ion is____; the number in a chloride ion is____.

(2) Write the atomic cores for potassium and chloride ions.

_____ _____

(3) Write the Lewis symbols for each ion.

_____ _____

(4)   Write the Lewis structure for the ionic compound potassium chloride in the box.

```
┌─────────────────┐
│                 │
│                 │
└─────────────────┘
```

Lewis structure of potassium chloride

(5)   How does the written Lewis structure for potassium chloride differ from that of hydrogen chloride?

4.   Construct the Lewis structure model for the covalent compound hydrogen sulfide (H_2S) using the following steps.

(1)   The total number of valence electrons in the two hydrogen atoms is _____; the sulfur atom has _____. Hence, the total number of valence electrons in the compound is _____.

(2)   Write the atomic cores for the hydrogen atoms and the sulfur atom in the space below. Because sulfur is the central atom in this molecule, arrange the cores so that the hydrogen atoms are on either side of the sulfur atom.

(3)   Rewrite the atomic cores in the space below. Place an electron pair between each hydrogen atom and the sulfur atom.

(4)   Write the Lewis structure for hydrogen sulfide in the box, distributing the remaining valence electrons so that the hydrogen atoms are in accordance with the duet rule and the sulfur atom is in accordance with the octet rule.

```
┌─────────────────┐
│                 │
│                 │
└─────────────────┘
```

Lewis structure of H_2S

5.   Construct the Lewis structure model for the covalent compound sulfur difluoride (SF_2) using the following steps.

(1)   The number of valence electrons in the sulfur atom is _____. The total number of valence electrons in the two fluorine atoms is _____. Hence, the total number of valence electrons in SF_2 is _____.

(2)   Arrange the atomic cores for the two fluorine atoms with the sulfur atom as the central atom in the space below.

(3)   Rewrite the atomic cores in the space below. Place an electron pair between each fluorine and sulfur core.

(4)   Write the Lewis structure for SF_2 in the box, distributing the remaining valence electrons so that all three atoms are in accordance with the octet rule.

```
┌─────────────────┐
│                 │
│                 │
└─────────────────┘
```

Lewis structure of SF_2

6.   Construct the Lewis structure model for the covalent compound methylene chloride (CH_2Cl_2).

(1)   The number of valence electrons in the carbon atom is _____. The total number of valence electrons in the two hydrogen atoms is _____. The total number of valence electrons in the two chlorine atoms is _____. Hence, the total number of valence electrons in CH_2Cl_2 is _____.

(2)   Position the atomic core for carbon as the central atom in the space below, and place the other cores around it.

(3)   Rewrite your arrangement of atomic cores in the space below, joining the cores with electron pairs to form the necessary bonds.

(4)   Write the Lewis structure for CH_2Cl_2 in the box, distributing the remaining valence electrons so that the carbon and chlorine atoms are in accordance with the octet rule and the H atoms in accordance with the duet rule.

Lewis structure of CH_2Cl_2

7. Construct the Lewis structure model for the covalent compound carbon tetrachloride (CCl_4) using the following steps.

(1)   The total number of valence electrons in CCl_4 is _____.

(2)   Write the atomic core for the element that seems most likely to be the central atom in the molecule in the space below. Position the remaining atomic cores around it.

(3)   Place an electron pair between each of the bonding atoms.

(4)   After distributing the remaining valence electrons so that the carbon and each chlorine atom has an electron octet, write the Lewis structure for CCl_4 in the box.

Lewis structure of CCl_4

8. Construct the Lewis structure model for the covalent compound phosgene ($COCl_2$) using the following steps.

(1)   The total number of valence electrons in $COCl_2$ is _____.

(2)   In this compound, carbon is the central atom. Arrange the atomic cores appropriately in the space below.

(3)   Add electron pairs to show the bonds between the atoms.

(4)   Assigning the remaining valence electrons so that each atom has an octet of electrons, write the Lewis structure for $COCl_2$ in the box. If you have trouble placing all of the valence electrons, consider the possibility of a multiple bond between two of the atoms.

Lewis structure of $COCl_2$

9. Construct the Lewis structure model for the covalent compound silicon dioxide (SiO_2) using the following steps.

(1)   The total number of valence electrons in SiO_2 is _____.

(2)   Arranging the atomic cores appropriately, write the Lewis structure for SiO_2 in the box. Use electron pairs to show the bonds between the atoms. Distribute the remaining electrons so that each atom has an octet.

(3)   If you have trouble placing all of the electrons, consider the possibility of using one or more double bonds in the structure. How many, if any, double bonds are required?

_____

Lewis structure of SiO_2

10. Write the Lewis structure for hydrosulfide ion (HS^-) in the box.

The total number of valence electrons in HS^- is

_____.

Lewis structure of HS^-

11. Write the Lewis structure for the covalent molecule nitrogen (N_2) in the box.

The total number of valence electrons in N_2 is

_____.

Lewis structure of N_2

II. Writing Chemical Equations Using Lewis Structures for Reactants and Products

1. Complete the following table. Assume that the first two pair of elements react to form ionic compounds and the third, a covalent compound. Refer to a periodic table in order to determine the number of valence electrons for each element. Write the empirical formula and the Lewis structure for each product.

2. Write both an equation using Lewis structures and a balanced chemical equation for the following reactions:

(1) Silicon atoms and chlorine molecules

(2) Lithium atoms and bromine molecules

(3) Ethylene molecules (C_2H_4) and chlorine molecules; the product is $C_2H_4Cl_2$. Recall the type of bond between the carbon atoms in ethylene, shown on p. 3, to help you to answer.

elements	number of valence electrons	empirical formula of product	Lewis structure of product
(1) potassium			
iodine			
(2) calcium			
fluorine			
(3) sulfur			
chlorine			

III. Predicting Empirical Formulas

1. The empirical formula for the hydride of sulfur is H_2S, and its central atom is sulfur. Based on this information, you would expect the empirical formula for the hydride of selenium, Se, to be

_____

and its Lewis structure to be

Lewis structure for hydride of selenium

2. The empirical formula for hydride of silicon is SiH_4, and its central atom is silicon. Based on this information, you would expect the empirical formula for hydride of tin to be

_____

and its Lewis structure to be

Lewis structure for hydride of tin

ISBN 0-87540-434-0

modular · laboratory · program · in · chemistry
program editor: H. A. Neidig

Naming Inorganic Compounds

prepared by **M. L. Gillette**, Indiana University Kokomo,
and **H. A. Neidig**, Lebanon Valley College

Purpose of the Experiment

Learn a systematic method for naming inorganic compounds.

Background Information

The same chemical compounds exist all over the world. Therefore, it is expedient to name these compounds in a way that is understood world-wide. To accomplish this, a naming system has been developed that has gained global acceptance. In this experiment, you will learn part of this nomenclature and apply its principles to the naming of a variety of inorganic compounds.

Naming a chemical compound is a systematic process. The first step is to note the kinds and amounts of elements in the compound, and the elements' locations on the periodic table. Recall that the periodic table is divided by a stair-step line into two parts, metals and nonmetals. Those elements to the left of the dividing line are metals; those elements to the right are nonmetals. The position of hydrogen (H) may vary, depending on the specific periodic table you use, but in terms of nomenclature, H is considered a nonmetal. Also of importance when naming a compound is the electronegativity of each element. Metals are much less electronegative than nonmetals.

Recognizing and Naming Elements

We divide chemical species into two broad categories, elements and compounds. When all the atoms in a chemical formula are the same kind, regardless of the number of atoms in the formula, we call the substance an **element**, and we name the substance by its elemental name. For example, Na is the elemental form of sodium, and Fe is the elemental form of iron. Elemental forms of nonmetals often include more than one atom. For example, O_2 is the elemental form of oxygen, and S_8 is the elemental form of sulfur.

Recognizing and Naming Compounds

Compounds are substances composed of at least two different elements combined chemically. Compounds composed of just two elements, such as a metal and a nonmetal, or two nonmetals, are called **binary compounds** such as NaCl and SO_2. Compounds composed of three elements are called **ternary compounds**. Ternary compounds consist of three nonmetals, two nonmetals and a metal, or one

nonmetal and two metals. Examples are $CaCO_3$, HNO_3, and $Al_2(SO_4)_3$.

Naming Binary Compounds

We divide binary compounds into two categories: ionic and covalent. An **ionic binary compound** contains a metal and a nonmetal. A **covalent binary compound** contains two nonmetals. We use similar systems of nomenclature to name the two types of binary compounds, as discussed below.

A. Naming Ionic Binary Compounds

To name an ionic binary compound, we place the name of the less electronegative element first, followed by the name of the more electronegative element, and we end the compound name with "-ide." Because metals are less electronegative than nonmetals, we begin with the name of the metal, then the name of the nonmetal. To help pronunciation, we shorten the nonmetal name and add an "-ide." For example, NaCl is an ionic binary compound. Sodium is a metal, so we place sodium first. We drop the "ine" from chlorine, and then add "ide," giving "sodium chloride." Similarly, the name of the ionic compound Na_2O is sodium oxide.

There are instances when, if we were to follow only this naming procedure, we would assign the same name to two different compounds. For example, CuO and Cu_2O are both copper oxides. To distinguish between these two compounds, we use the Stock nomenclature system. The Stock system includes the oxidation numbers of the elements in the compound as part of the compound's name. The **oxidation number** of an atom in a compound describes the electron distribution around the atom, assuming that all of the electrons in the surrounding chemical bonds are associated with the more electronegative element. We recognize that this assumption is a simplification, because electrons are, at least to some extent, shared in most chemical bonds. However, the process of assigning oxidation numbers can still be very useful. Rules for determining the oxidation number of each element in a compound are given in Table 1. To be useful, the rules must be applied in order.

Applying the oxidation number rules 4 and 8 to the Stock nomenclature system, we find that the oxidation number of oxygen is –2 in both CuO and Cu_2O. Therefore, the oxidation number of Cu in CuO must be +2, and the oxidation number of Cu in Cu_2O must be +1. In the Stock system, we write the Cu oxidation numbers as Roman numerals in parentheses in the formula next to the name "copper" to distinguish between the two

Table 1 Rules for determining the oxidation numbers of the elements in a compound
1.   The oxidation number of an element (uncombined, or combined only with itself, such as Ne, Br_2, S_8) is zero.
2.   The oxidation number of a monatomic ion such as Ag^+ or Fe^{3+} is equal to its ionic charge. For example, the oxidation number of Zn^{2+} ion is +2.
3.   Because it is the most electronegative element, fluorine, when combined with any other element, has the oxidation number –1. Unless they are combined with a more electronegative element, the other halogens also have the oxidation number –1.
4.   The sum of the oxidation numbers for a chemical species must equal the net charge on the species. For example, the net charge on the permanganate ion (MnO_4^-), indicated by a superscript minus, is –1. This is equal to the sum of the oxidation numbers: $Mn^{7+} + 4(O^{2-}) = MnO_4^- = +7 + (4)(-2) = -1$.
5.   Aluminum and gallium in compounds have the oxidation number +3.
6.   When they are part of compounds, the alkali and alkaline earth metals have the oxidation numbers +1 and +2, respectively.
7.   When combined with nonmetals, hydrogen has the oxidation number +1. Examples include CH_4, H_2S, and HCl. In metal hydrides, such as NaH and CaH_2, the oxidation number of hydrogen is –1.
8.   Oxygen is the second most electronegative element. When combined with other elements, oxygen usually has the oxidation number –2. Exceptions are peroxides, such as H_2O_2, where the oxidation number of oxygen is –1, and superoxides, which end in O_2^-, where the oxidation number of oxygen is –1/2.

compounds. Thus, we name CuO as copper(II) oxide, and Cu_2O as copper(I) oxide. We omit the Roman numeral in names of compounds containing atoms that have only one possible oxidation number. For example, the name of Na_2O is sodium oxide, not sodium(I) oxide, because sodium has only one possible oxidation number.

B. Naming Covalent Binary Compounds

We use a system similar to the Stock system to name covalent binary compounds. We begin the same way, naming the less electronegative element first, then the more electronegative element, and ending the compound name with "-ide." We can also use oxidation numbers to distinguish different compounds containing the same elements. For example, SO_2 is sulfur(IV) oxide, and SO_3 is sulfur(VI) oxide. However, because of the large number of covalent compounds some nonmetals form with oxygen, an alternative nomenclature was developed in which the number of each atom present in the atom is added as a prefix to the name of that element. The standard prefixes include "mono" for *one*, "di" for *two*, "tri" for *three*, "tetra" for *four*, and so on. For example, we could call SO_2 sulfur dioxide and SO_3 sulfur trioxide. Nitrogen and oxygen form a series of oxides, including NO and N_2O. We could call NO nitrogen monoxide and N_2O dinitrogen monoxide.

When covalent binary compounds composed of hydrogen and another more electronegative nonmetal dissolve in water, a hydrogen ion is transferred from the binary compound to the water, forming a hydronium ion (H_3O^+) and the anion of the nonmetal. Therefore, in aqueous solution, the compound functions as an acid. In naming the compound, we indicate its acidic function by adding the prefix "hydro" and changing the "ide" suffix to "ic acid." For example, hydrogen chloride (HCl) which is a gas at room temperature, dissolves in water to produce hydrochloric acid, HCl(aq). Similarly, H_2S is called dihydrogen sulfide unless it is dissolved in water, in which case we represented it by H_2S(aq) and call it hydrosulfuric acid.

Naming Ternary Compounds

A large number of ternary compounds are either acids containing polyatomic anions or salts of those acids. A **polyatomic anion** is a group of different types of atoms, usually including oxygen, that is covalently bonded. Polyatomic ions generally carry a net charge of −1, −2, or −3. The non-oxygen atoms in the polyatomic ion can be a metal, as in permanganate ion, MnO_4^-, or a nonmetal, as in phosphate ion, PO_4^{3-}. The formulas and names of some commonly occurring polyatomic anions are shown in Table 2 on the next page. Because the name of a polyatomic ion is based on the oxidation number of either the structurally central atom or the non-oxygen atom in the ion, these oxidation numbers are included in the table. Table 2 also includes the ammonium ion, NH_4^+, the only common example of a polyatomic cation, plus the common names of some of the ions, in parentheses. The two columns on the right list the name of the acid containing the ion and the formula of the acid.

There are an enormous number of compounds composed of carbon, hydrogen, and oxygen. These compounds are sometimes classified as "organic," and there is an extensive nomenclature specifically associated with them. Although the nomenclature for organic compounds is not included in this module, several organic ions are so pervasive that they are included in this list.

A. Naming Ternary Acids

As you can see from the ions listed in Table 2, oxygen can combine with other atoms in several different proportions. We base the nomenclature for these combinations on the oxidation number of the non-oxygen atom. Consider the series of compounds HClO, $HClO_2$, $HClO_3$, and $HClO_4$. The oxidation numbers of chlorine in these compounds are +1, +3, +5, and +7, respectively. When the non-oxygen element is in a higher oxidation state, we end the name with "ic," and when it is in a lower oxidation state, we end the name with "ous." When the non-oxygen element in an ion in such a series is in its lowest oxidation state, we use the prefix "hypo" (along with the "-ous" suffix), and when the element is in its highest oxidation state, we use the prefix "per" (along with the suffix "-ic"). Thus, the acids in the above series are named hypochlorous acid (HClO), chlorous acid ($HClO_2$), chloric acid ($HClO_3$), and perchloric acid ($HClO_4$).

B. Naming Ternary Salts

Ternary salts are compounds formed when one or more of the hydrogen atoms in a ternary acid are replaced by metal ions. We name these compounds by writing the name of the cation first, then the anion, just as we did for binary compounds. As you can see from Table 2, the anion ending depends on the oxidation state of that element in the polyatomic anion. If the name of the parent acid ends in "ic," then the name of the anion ends in "ate." If the name of the parent acid ends in "ous," then the name of the anion ends in "ite."

For example, Na_2SO_4 and Na_2SO_3 are salts of H_2SO_4 (sulfuric acid) and H_2SO_3 (sulfurous acid), respectively. Thus, we call Na_2SO_4 sodium sulfate and Na_2SO_3 sodium sulfite. The names of $NaHSO_4$ and $NaHSO_3$ are sodium hydrogen sulfate (or, commonly, sodium bisulfate) and sodium hydrogen sulfite (or, commonly, sodium bisulfite). When the cation replacing hydrogen in the acid can have various oxidation states, we specify the current oxidation state in the name, just as we did for binary compounds. For example, $CuSO_4$ is copper(II) sulfate and $Fe_2(SO_4)_3$ is iron(III) sulfate.

Table 2 *Some common polyatomic ions*

ion name	chemical formula	central atom oxidation number		acid name	acid formula
acetate*	$C_2H_3O_2^-$	C:	+1	acetic acid	$HC_2H_3O_2$
ammonium	NH_4^+	N:	−3	ammonium ion	NH_4^+
carbonate*	CO_3^{2-}	C:	+4	carbonic acid	H_2CO_3
chlorate	ClO_3^-	Cl:	+5	chloric acid	$HClO_3$
chlorite	ClO_2^-	Cl:	+3	chlorous acid	$HClO_2$
chromate	CrO_4^{2-}	Cr:	+6	chromic acid	H_2CrO_4
cyanide*	CN^-	C:	+2	hydrocyanic acid	HCN
dichromate	$Cr_2O_7^{2-}$	Cr:	+6	dichromic acid	$H_2Cr_2O_7$
dihydrogen phosphate	$H_2PO_4^-$	P:	+5	phosphoric acid	H_3PO_4
hydrogen carbonate* (bicarbonate)	HCO_3^-	C:	+4	carbonic acid	H_2CO_3
hydrogen phosphate	HPO_4^{2-}	P:	+5	phosphoric acid	H_3PO_4
hydrogen sulfate (bisulfate)	HSO_4^-	S:	+7	sulfuric acid	H_2SO_4
hydrogen sulfite (bisulfite)	HSO_3^-	S:	+4	sulfurous acid	H_2SO_3
hydroxide	OH^-	O:	−2	water	H_2O
hypochlorite	ClO^-	Cl:	+1	hypochlorous acid	$HClO$
perchlorate	ClO_4^-	Cl:	+7	perchloric acid	$HClO_4$
permanganate	MnO_4^-	Mn:	+7	permanganic acid	$HMnO_4$
nitrite	NO_2^-	N:	+3	nitrous acid	HNO_2
nitrate	NO_3^-	N:	+5	nitric acid	HNO_3
oxalate*	$C_2O_4^{2-}$	C:	+3	oxalic acid	$H_2C_2O_4$
peroxide	O_2^{2-}	O:	−1	hydrogen peroxide	H_2O_2
phosphate	PO_4^{3-}	P:	+5	phosphoric acid	H_3PO_4
sulfate	SO_4^{2-}	S:	+6	sulfuric acid	H_2SO_4
sulfite	SO_3^{2-}	S:	+4	sulfurous acid	H_2SO_3

*organic compounds

Naming Hydrates

When ionic compounds crystallize, water molecules frequently occupy sites in the crystal lattice. These water molecules, called **waters of hydration**, become part of the chemical makeup of the compound. For example, copper(II) sulfate can crystallize to form a lattice containing five H_2O molecules for every Cu^{2+} ion and SO_4^{2-} ion pair. When this occurs, we write the chemical formula of the compound as $CuSO_4 \cdot 5\ H_2O$. We include the H_2O molecules in the name of the crystallized compound by writing "hydrate" after the compound name and adding a standard prefix to "hydrate" to indicate the number of H_2O molecules per ion. Thus, $CuSO_4 \cdot 5\ H_2O$ is called copper(II) sulfate pentahydrate.

Naming Compounds Containing a Complex Ion

When ionic transition metal compounds dissolve, the cation is often stabilized through formation of coordinate covalent bonds with Lewis bases, or **ligands**, in solution. We call the product of such a stabilization a **complex ion**, or, if the product has no charge, a **coordination complex**. For example, $[Ag(NH_3)_2]^+$ and $[CoCl_4]^{2-}$ are complex ions and $[Ag(NH_3)_2]Cl$ and $K_2[CoCl_4]$ are coordination complexes. The species enclosed in brackets is covalently bonded and exists as a polyatomic ion in solution. Note that complex ions can have either a positive or negative charge; that is, they can be cations or anions.

Table 3 *Names and formulas of some common ligands*

A. Monodentate Ligands

name	formula		name	formula
aquo-	H_2O		hydroxo-	OH^-
ammine-	NH_3		iodo-	I^-
bromo-	Br^-		nitro-	NO_2^-
chloro-	Cl^-		thiocyanato-	SCN^-
cyano-	CN^-		fluoro-	F^-

B. Bidentate Ligands

name	formula		name and formula
oxalato-	$C_2O_4^{2-}$		ethylenediamine (en)
			$NH_2CH_2CH_2NH_2$

C. Polydentate Ligand

ethylenediaminetetraacetic acid (EDTA)

When discussing ligands that are part of complex ions or coordination complexes, we call ligands that have one shared electron pair on the central metal ion **monodentate ligands**. A ligand that has two coordinate covalent bonds on the central metal cation is a **bidentate ligand**. Some ligands can have as many as six bonds on the central metal cation. Ligands with more than two bonds on the metal cation are called **polydentate ligands**. The formulas and names of some Lewis bases commonly encountered as ligands in complex ion and coordination complexes are listed in Table 3. You will note some slight spelling changes in the names of ions serving as ligands.

As with previously discussed nomenclatures, when we name coordination compounds, we place the cation name first, and then the anion name. When we name the complex ion portion, we list the ligands first, then the central metal ion. If a ligand is an anion, we add an "o" to its name, as in "fluoro" for F^- ion. We specify the number of ligands with the same prefixes used to specify number of hydrates: mono-, di-, tri-, tetra-, penta-, and hexa- for 1 through 6, respectively. If the ligand name contains "di-," "tri-," or "tetra-," we use the prefixes bis-, tris-, and tetrakis-, respectively. The name for the metal ion depends on whether the ion is part of an anionic or cationic complex ion. If the complex ion has a positive charge, we use the usual name of the metal. If the complex has a negative charge, we add an "-ate" after the metal name, or, in some cases, we identify the metal ion by its Latin name. These Latin names are given in Table 4. In either case, we use a Roman numeral in parentheses to designate the oxidation number of the metal ion. If a metal ion is complexed with more than one kind of ligand, we list the ligands alphabetically, ignoring the prefixes.

Table 4 *Latin names for metal ions in anionic complexes*

metal	chemical symbol	name when metal is in anionic complex
copper	Cu	cuprate
gold	Au	aurate
iron	Fe	ferrate
lead	Pb	plumbate
silver	Ag	argentate
tin	Sn	stannate

To illustrate these naming principles, let us name the two coordination compounds, $[Cu(H_2O)_6]Cl_2$ and $K_2[CoCl_4]$. In the case of $[Cu(H_2O)_6]Cl_2$, we know that the complex ion is a cation with a charge of +2, because two Cl^- ions are required to make up a neutral compound. We can also determine that the oxidation state of Cu is +2, because the ligands, H_2O, are uncharged. We name the cation by first naming the ligands, using a prefix to indicate the number, then the metal ion and its oxidation number. Thus, the name of the cation is hexaaquocopper(II). Then we name the anion, chloride. Hence, the name of $[Cu(H_2O)_6]Cl_2$ is hexaaquocopper(II) chloride.

We name $K_2[CoCl_4]$ by first determining that the complex ion portion has a −2 charge, because two K^+ ions are required to balance the charge on the complex ion. Furthermore, Co must be in a +2 oxidation state in

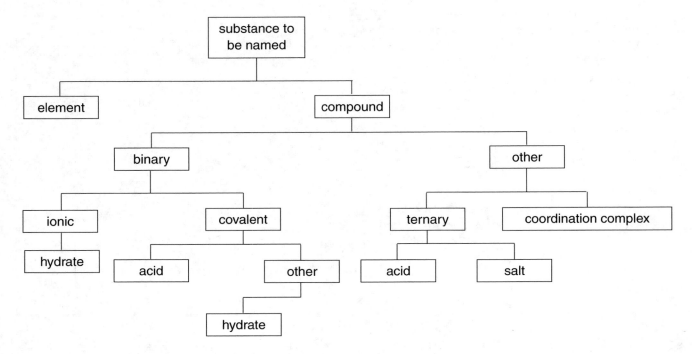

Figure 1   *Overall naming procedure*

the complex, because the combination of +2 and the four Cl^- ions is required to produce an overall charge of −2 on the complex ion. We name the cation first, potassium. We name the anion by first listing the ligands, tetrachloro, and then the metal, ending the name with "-ate" and the oxidation number: cobaltate(II). Hence, $K_2[CoCl_4]$ is potassium tetrachlorocobaltate(II). Using the same approach, we call $[Co(NH_3)_4Cl_2]Cl$ tetraamminedichlorocobalt(III) chloride.

Approaching Nomenclature Systematically

While each of the above sets of naming rules may seem clear by itself, we still need an overall procedure for naming compounds. The flowchart shown in Figure 1 outlines such a procedure.

Exercise Set 1

1. Determine the oxidation number of the metal atom or ion in each of the following compounds:

    (1) MnF_3 oxidation number   _____

    (2) FeO oxidation number   _____

    (3) Hg_2Cl_2 oxidation number   _____

    (4) Li_3N oxidation number   _____

    (5) Fe_2O_3 oxidation number   _____

2. Name the following ionic binary compounds:

    (1) $BaBr_2$ _____

    (2) K_2O _____

    (3) $CaCl_2$ _____

    (4) Fe_2O_3 _____

    (5) FeO _____

name ____________ section ____________ date ____________

Exercise Set 2

1. Name the following covalent binary compounds:

(1) HCl(aq) ____________

(2) N_2O_5 ____________

(3) HBr(aq) ____________

(4) PCl_5 ____________

2. Write the chemical formulas for the following binary compounds:

(1) silicon carbide ____________

(2) carbon disulfide ____________

(3) sulfur hexafluoride ____________

Exercise Set 3

1. Name the following ternary acids:

(1) $HBrO_3$ ____________

(2) HBrO ____________

(3) HIO_4 ____________

2. Write the formulas of the following ternary acids:

(1) iodous acid ____________

(2) iodic acid ____________

(3) hypoiodous acid ____________

Exercise Set 4

1. Name the following ternary salts:

(1) $Fe(ClO_4)_3$ ____________

(2) $Al_2(SO_4)_3$ ____________

(3) Cu_2CO_3 ____________

2. Write the formulas for the following ternary salts:

(1) ammonium phosphate ____________

(2) lead(II) acetate ____________

(3) manganese(II) hydroxide ____________

Exercise Set 5

1. Name the following hydrates:

(1) $NiBr_2 \cdot 3\,H_2O$ ____________

(2) $CaCl_2 \cdot 2\,H_2O$ ____________

2. Write the formula for the following hydrates:

  (1)   manganese(II) acetate tetrahydrate   _____

  (2)   iron(II) nitrate hexahydrate   _____

Exercise Set 6

1. Name the following coordination compounds:

  (1) $[Mo(H_2O)_6]Br_3$ _____

  (2) $K[Co(C_2O_4)_2(H_2O)_2]$ _____

  (3) $[Fe(NH_3)_2(NO_2)_2]_2SO_4$ _____

2. Write the formulas for the following coordination compounds:

  (1)   potassium hexacyanoferrate(III)   _____

  (2)   pentaamminechlorocobalt(III) chloride   _____

  (3)   sodium bromochlorodicyanatonickelate(II)   _____

  (4)   tetraamminedichloroplatinum(IV) tetrachloroplatinate(II)   _____

Exercise Set 7   Review Exercises

1. Name the following:

  (1) O_2 _____

  (2) Ta_2O_5 _____

  (3) $NaHSO_4$ _____

  (4) $LiClO_4 \cdot 3\,H_2O$ _____

  (5) $[Cr(NH_3)_5Br](C_2H_3O_2)_2$ _____

  (6) $Ca(ClO)_2$ _____

2. Write the formulas for the following:

  (1)   hydrobromic acid   _____

  (2)   potassium hydrogen phosphate   _____

  (3)   hydrogen iodide trihydrate   _____

  (4)   ammonium tetrachlorozincate(II)   _____

  (5)   calcium hydrogen sulfate   _____

  (6)   bromous acid   _____

ISBN 0-87540-459-6

modular · laboratory · program · in · chemistry

program editor: Conrad L. Stanitski

Using Exponential Notation and Significant Figures

prepared by **Norman E. Griswold**, Nebraska Wesleyan University

---

Purpose of the Experiment

Review exponential notation and use it to solve problems with and without a calculator. Review rules for determining significant figures and use them to round off calculations.

Background Information

I.   Exponential Notation

During your study of chemistry, you will encounter numbers ranging from the incredibly large to the extremely small. For example, a 100-mL sample of water contains more than 3 septillion molecules of water, or 3,000,000,000,000,000,000,000,000 molecules. Each water molecule has a mass of approximately 30 septillionths of a gram, or 0.000 000 000 000 000 000 000 000 03 grams. Representing very large or very small numbers this way is awkward and time consuming. Consequently, we usually use exponential notation, sometimes called **scientific notation**, to express such numbers.

A.   Expressing Numbers Using Exponential Notation

Exponential notation expresses numbers as the product of two factors. The first factor, the **digit term**, is a number between 1 and 10. The digit term is

multiplied by the second factor, called the **exponential term**, which has the form 10^x, 10 raised to a specific whole number power called the **exponent**.

For example, using exponential notation we represent 126 as 1.26×10^2, which we read as "one point two six times ten to the second". As shown in Figure 1, the digit term in this expression is 1.26. This term includes all the significant figures of the number being represented. (We will review the rules for determining significant figures in Part II of this module.)

$$1.26 \times 10^2 \longleftarrow \text{exponent}$$

digit term   exponential term

Figure 1   *Exponential notation*

The exponential term in this example is 10^2. A positive exponent represents the number of times the digit term must be *multiplied* by 10 to give the number represented. For example, 1.26×10^2 means $1.26 \times 10 \times 10 = 126$. Note that there are three figures in the digit term and three figures in the number being represented.

Some additional examples of numbers expressed in exponential notation are:

$$273.15 = 2.7315 \times 10^2$$
$$0.08206 = 8.206 \times 10^{-2}$$
$$0.001 = 1 \times 10^{-3}$$

These examples show that, when expressed using exponential notation, numbers greater than 10 have positive exponents and numbers less than 1 have negative exponents.

A negative exponent represents the number of times the digit term must be **divided** by 10 to give the number being represented. Thus, 2.46×10^{-3} means

$$2.46 \times \frac{1}{10} \times \frac{1}{10} \times \frac{1}{10} = 0.00246$$

Another way to interpret the exponent is to say that the exponent is equal to the number of places we must move the decimal point in a number to convert the number into the digit term. If the decimal point must be moved to the **left**, the exponent is positive. For example, the number 126 can be expressed as 1.26×10^2. The decimal point (following the 6 in 126) must be moved two places to the left to give the digit term, 1.26, so the exponent is a positive 2.

If the decimal point must be moved to the **right**, the exponent is negative. As another example, 0.00246 can be expressed as 2.46×10^{-3}. The exponential term is 10^{-3}, because the decimal point in 0.00246 must be moved three places to the right to give the digit term, 2.46. We could also express 0.00246 as 24.6×10^{-4}, 246×10^{-5}, or even as 0.246×10^{-2}. However, scientists usually keep the digit term between 1 and 10. For this example then, 2.46×10^{-3} is preferred, although the other expressions are acceptable.

B. Exponential Notation Using a Calculator

An electronic calculator is an important aid for performing chemical calculations. Your calculator may be slightly different from the one used for the following examples. If so, use your calculator's instruction book when performing these tasks.

To use exponential notation with your calculator, it must have an exponent key, usually labeled $\boxed{\text{EXP}}$ (or $\boxed{\text{EE}}$ or $\boxed{\text{EEX}}$ on some models).

1. Entering Exponential Numbers on a Calculator
To enter 1.26×10^2 on a calculator with an $\boxed{\text{EXP}}$ key, press the following keys in the order shown.

$$\boxed{1}\ \boxed{\bullet}\ \boxed{2}\ \boxed{6}\ \boxed{\text{EXP}}\ \boxed{2}$$

To enter 2.46×10^{-3} on a calculator with an $\boxed{\text{EXP}}$ key, press the following keys in order.

$$\boxed{2}\ \boxed{\bullet}\ \boxed{4}\ \boxed{6}\ \boxed{\text{EXP}}\ \boxed{+/-}\ \boxed{3}$$

The $\boxed{+/-}$ key may be labeled $\boxed{\text{CHS}}$ for "change sign".

Some calculators can be set so that the answers are automatically expressed in exponential notation on the display. If your calculator has the appropriate keys, select the exponential notation mode by pressing $\boxed{\text{2nd}}$, then $\boxed{\text{SCI}}$. Other calculators require different keystrokes to select the exponential notation mode.

The following example shows the different answers obtained using the normal mode and the exponential notation mode.

normal mode: $(3.2 \times 10^{-3}) \times (5 \times 10^{-4}) = 0.0000016$

exponential notation mode: $(3.2 \times 10^{-3}) \times (5 \times 10^{-4})$
$$= 1.6 \times 10^{-6}$$

2. Adding, Subtracting, Multiplying, and Dividing Exponential Expressions
In order to use a calculator to add, subtract, multiply, or divide exponential expressions, we use the keys $\boxed{+}$, $\boxed{-}$, $\boxed{\times}$, or $\boxed{\div}$, which represent these operations, just as we would when manipulating numbers in normal notation. The only difference is that you must first select exponential notation mode. For example, use the following sequence of keystrokes to calculate $(3.2 \times 10^{-3}) \times (5 \times 10^{-4})$.

$$\boxed{3}\ \boxed{\bullet}\ \boxed{2}\ \boxed{\text{EXP}}\ \boxed{+/-}\ \boxed{3}\ \boxed{\times}\ \boxed{5}\ \boxed{\text{EXP}}\ \boxed{+/-}\ \boxed{4}\ \boxed{=} = 1.6 \times 10^{-6}$$

3. Determining Square Roots and Cube Roots of Exponential Expressions
To obtain square roots of exponential numbers, remember that $\sqrt{A} = A^{1/2}$ and use the $\boxed{\sqrt{x}}$ or $\boxed{y^x}$ key. For calculators with a $\boxed{y^x}$ key, use the following sequence of keystrokes to find the square root of 2.7×10^{10}.

$$\boxed{2}\ \boxed{\bullet}\ \boxed{7}\ \boxed{\text{EXP}}\ \boxed{1}\ \boxed{0}\ \boxed{y^x}\ \boxed{\bullet}\ \boxed{5}\ \boxed{=} = 1.6 \times 10^5$$

The $\boxed{\bullet}$ and $\boxed{5}$ keystrokes are used because $\frac{1}{2} = 0.5$.

To obtain cube roots of exponential numbers, remember that $\sqrt[3]{A} = A^{1/3} = A^{0.333}$, and use the $\boxed{y^x}$ key. For example, to take the cube root of 2.7×10^{10}, use the following sequence of keystrokes.

$$\boxed{2}\ \boxed{\bullet}\ \boxed{7}\ \boxed{\text{EXP}}\ \boxed{1}\ \boxed{0}\ \boxed{y^x}\ \boxed{\bullet}\ \boxed{3}\ \boxed{3}\ \boxed{3}\ \boxed{=} = 2.97 \times 10^3$$

4. Taking Logarithms and Antilogs of Exponential Numbers
A logarithm is an exponent: It is the power to which 10 must be raised in order to produce a given number. For example, $1.5 \times 10^4 = 10^{4.18}$. The given number is 1.5×10^4, and its logarithm is 4.18. The logarithm of 1.5×10^4, written as $\log 1.5 \times 10^4$, can be determined by the following sequence of keystrokes.

$$\boxed{1}\ \boxed{\bullet}\ \boxed{5}\ \boxed{\text{EXP}}\ \boxed{4}\ \boxed{\log} = 4.18$$

The reverse of obtaining ("taking") a logarithm is taking the antilog. To take the antilog of 4.18, select the exponential notation mode on your calculator. Then use the following keystrokes to calculate antilog $10^{4.18}$.

$$\boxed{1}\boxed{0}\boxed{y^x}\boxed{4}\boxed{\cdot}\boxed{1}\boxed{8}\boxed{=} = 1.5 \times 10^4$$

If your calculator is not set for exponential notation mode, the answer will appear as 15135.612.

C. Using Exponential Numbers without a Calculator

1. Adding and Subtracting Exponential Numbers To add or subtract exponential numbers without a calculator, the numbers must have the same exponents. Consider the following example: $(1.27 \times 10^3) + (4 \times 10^1)$. One way to express these numbers so that they have identical exponents is to rewrite 4×10^1 as 0.04×10^3. Moving the decimal point two places to the left increases the exponent by two. The example then becomes $(1.27 \times 10^3) + (0.04 \times 10^3)$. Next, add the digit terms, the sum of which becomes the digit term of the answer. The final answer is the answer digit term multiplied by the common exponential term, as shown.

$$
\begin{array}{ll}
1.27 \times 10^3 & \longrightarrow \quad 1.27 \times 10^3 \\
+\underline{\quad 4 \times 10^1} & \longrightarrow +\underline{0.04 \times 10^3} \\
& \qquad\qquad 1.31 \times 10^3
\end{array}
$$

The following is the result if we rewrite 1.27×10^3, rather than 4×10^1, before adding.

$$
\begin{array}{ll}
1.27 \times 10^3 & \longrightarrow \quad 127 \times 10^1 \\
+\underline{\quad 4 \times 10^1} & \longrightarrow +\underline{\quad 4 \times 10^1} \\
& \quad 131 \times 10^1 = 1.31 \times 10^3
\end{array}
$$

The answer is the same: It does not matter which number we change before addition. However, the first method directly gives the result in preferred exponential form (only one digit to the left of the decimal point).

The rules for subtraction of exponential numbers are the same as for addition, except that the digit terms are subtracted rather than added. Here are two examples:

$$
\begin{array}{ll}
1.0 \times 10^2 & \longrightarrow \quad 10 \times 10^1 \\
-\underline{\quad 4 \times 10^1} & \longrightarrow -\underline{\quad 4 \times 10^1} \\
& \qquad\qquad 6 \times 10^1
\end{array}
$$

$$
\begin{array}{ll}
3.2 \times 10^{-3} & \longrightarrow \quad 3.2 \times 10^{-3} \\
-\underline{\quad 5 \times 10^{-4}} & \longrightarrow -\underline{0.5 \times 10^{-3}} \\
& \qquad\qquad 2.7 \times 10^{-3}
\end{array}
$$

2. Multiplying Exponential Numbers When multiplying or dividing exponential numbers without a calculator, it is not necessary for the numbers to have identical exponents. To multiply exponential numbers, first multiply the digit terms. Then **add** the exponents to obtain the exponential term of the answer. A general expression for this procedure is:

$$(A \times 10^n)(B \times 10^m) = (A \times B) \times 10^{n+m}$$

Here are some specific examples:

$$(2 \times 10^4)(4 \times 10^2) = (2 \times 4) \times 10^{4+2} = 8 \times 10^6$$

$$(2 \times 10^4)(4 \times 10^{-2}) = (2 \times 4) \times 10^{4+(-2)} = 8 \times 10^2$$

$$(2 \times 10^{-4})(4 \times 10^{-2}) = (2 \times 4) \times 10^{(-4)+(-2)} = 8 \times 10^{-6}$$

Sometimes multiplying exponential numbers results in an answer in which the exponential term is 10^0. In such cases, remember that $10^0 = 1$ exactly; the exponential term can be dropped from the answer. For example:

$$(2 \times 10^4)(4 \times 10^{-4}) = (2 \times 4) \times 10^{4+(-4)} = 8 \times 10^0 = 8$$

3. Dividing Exponential Numbers To divide exponential numbers, first divide the digit terms. Then **subtract** the exponent of the denominator from the exponent of the numerator to obtain the exponent of the answer. A general expression of this procedure is:

$$\frac{A \times 10^n}{B \times 10^m} = \frac{A}{B} \times 10^{n-m}$$

Some specific examples are:

$$\frac{6 \times 10^4}{3 \times 10^2} = \frac{6}{3} \times 10^{4-2} = 2 \times 10^2$$

$$\frac{6 \times 10^4}{3 \times 10^{-2}} = \frac{6}{3} \times 10^{4-(-2)} = 2 \times 10^6$$

$$\frac{6 \times 10^{-4}}{3 \times 10^{-2}} = \frac{6}{3} \times 10^{(-4)-(-2)} = 2 \times 10^{-2}$$

II. Significant Figures

One of the first concepts taught in chemistry is **density**, the mass of a substance divided by its volume. Suppose that, to help understand density, you are asked to determine the density of a metal sample as accurately as possible. Using an analytical balance, you determine the mass of the assigned metal sample as 14.3216 g. If its volume is 2.00 mL, what should you report as the density of the metal?

When more than 100 students were asked this question, they gave the following answers: 7.1608 (most common), 7.160, 7.161, 7.16, 7.1, 7.2, and "about 7." Are all these answers correct? If not, which is correct? Would these answers have differed if the mass had been reported as 14 g? How can you report experimental results in a way that indicates the exactness of the measurements involved? All these questions can be resolved by using some simple rules to determine the proper number of figures to use when reporting a result obtained from measurements. The proper number of figures to include are called **significant figures** or **significant numbers**.

The basic rule for determining significant figures is: **only those figures that are reasonably reliable are significant**. The following sections describe how to determine which figures in a measurement are reasonably reliable and, therefore, are significant figures.

A. Kinds of Experimental Values

Experimental values in chemistry consist of two broad groups: **exact numbers** and **inexact numbers**. The first group includes numbers that arise from counting or from certain definitions. For example, if we count the students in a chemistry class, we know the exact number of people in the class. Similarly, some numerical relationships are exact by definition. Such numbers can be thought of as having an infinite number of significant figures. Some examples include:

$$1.000 \text{ L} = 1000 \text{ mL}$$
$$1.000 \text{ cm} = 1.00 \times 10^7 \text{ nm}$$
$$1.00 \text{ g} = 1.00 \times 10^{-3} \text{ kg}$$

By definition, 1.000 liter is **exactly** equal to 1000 milliliters. These examples are all conversions within a given system of units, in this case, the metric system.

The second group, inexact numbers, consists of numbers resulting from measurements and approximate conversion factors. The exactness of a measurement depends upon the measuring device. For example, Figure 2 shows arrows positioned at identical locations on three scales that differ only in the number of measuring marks. In Figure 2(a), the estimated position of the arrow is 6 or 7. A more exact position cannot be obtained using the scale in Figure 2(a). Figure 2(b) shows that the arrow is slightly closer to 7 than to 6. Using the scale in Figure 2(b), we can estimate that the arrow is at 6.5 or 6.6. The scale in Figure 2(c) makes it clear that the arrow is closer to 6.6 than to 6.5. Using the scale in Figure 2(c), a reasonable estimate for the arrow position is about 6.58 or 6.59. As you can see, the exactness of a measurement depends on the measuring device.

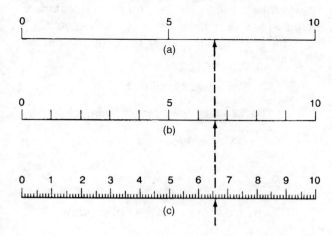

Figure 2 *Examples of measurement using scales of varying precision*

Certain conversion factors are also inexact. This situation occurs when converting from one system of units to another system, such as converting from the English system to the metric system. For example, by definition, the conversion of the mass unit called the English pound to the metric kilogram is:

$$1.00 \text{ lb} = 0.45359237 \text{ kg}$$

However, a more common (but less exact) conversion factor found in many tables is:

$$1 \text{ lb} = 0.4536 \text{ kg}$$

The number of significant figures in 0.45359237 and 0.4536 is different. Rules for determining the correct number of significant figures to use when reporting a measurement or calculation are given in the following section.

B. Determining the Number of Significant Figures

A reasonably reliable measurement contains at least one figure that is known with certainty, plus one estimated figure to the right of the last known figure. In Figure 2(b), for example, a reasonably reliable estimate of the arrow position is 6.6, although the arrow could be at either 6.5 or 6.7. In this case, the ones figure is known with certainty, and the tenths figure is estimated. Therefore, based on Figure 2(b), the number 6.6 contains two significant figures. If we were to report 6.62 as the arrow position for Figure 2(b), the second estimated figure, 2, would not be significant. In a reasonably reliable estimate, only one estimated figure can be included among the significant figures reported.

Similarly, for reported measurements or results, we assume that only the last numeral is estimated. Based on this assumption, it is not hard to determine the number of significant figures in reported values. For example,

1.75 has 3 significant figures

1.754 has 4 significant figures

17.54 has 4 significant figures

The following two rules apply to correctly reported values.

1. All nonzero numerals are counted as significant figures.

2. The position of the decimal point has no effect on the number of significant figures, as long as the number contains no zeros.

For numbers containing zeros, common sense is very useful for determining the number of significant figures. For example, 2.016 clearly contains four significant figures: The zero is in the middle of the number, so it must be included. On the other hand, with small numbers like 0.08206 and large numbers like 135,000, there can be some confusion about whether zeros at the beginning or the end of a number should be counted. The following rules apply to counting zeros as significant figures.

3. Zeros to the left of all nonzero numerals are not significant.

This means that you start counting significant figures at the nonzero numeral farthest to the left in the number, and count to the right. The following examples illustrate this rule:

0.0821 contains 3 significant figures (start counting at the 8 and count to the right)

0.002 has one significant figure (start counting at the 2)

4. Zeros surrounded by nonzero numerals are significant.

The following examples illustrate this rule:

200.59 has 5 significant figures

2.016 has 4 significant figures

0.08206 has 4 significant figures (start counting at the 8)

Note again that the position of the decimal point does not affect the number of significant figures.

5. Zeros to the right of all nonzero numerals, called *trailing zeros*, may or may not be significant.

(a) If a decimal point appears in the number, all trailing zeros to the right of the decimal point are significant. For example:

0.00640 has 3 significant figures (start counting at the 6; the last zero is to the right of all the nonzero digits and to the right of the decimal point; it is therefore significant)

75.0 has 3 significant figures (same reasoning)

1000.0 has 5 significant figures (all zeros are significant, because the last one is to the right of the decimal point)

(b) If trailing zeros are all to the left of the decimal point, then we must know more about the number to determine whether any of these zeros are significant. Sometimes a reasonable guess is necessary. The following examples clarify this rule.

The number 1000 may contain from one to four significant figures. For example, if you lift an object with your hand and guess that it weighs about 1000 g, this is obviously not an exact measurement. In this case, the measurement and the number has only one significant figure, the 1. If you weigh the same object on a balance that determines mass to the nearest 10 g, then you can be reasonably certain of the first three figures in the measurement. In this case, 1000 has 3 significant figures. If you weigh the object on a balance that determines mass to the nearest gram, then all four figures in 1000 are significant.

As another example, the number 135,000 oz probably represents an approximate measurement, so it likely has only 3 significant figures. The zeros probably are there only to show the position of the decimal point. In cases like this, we cannot be sure whether any of the zeros are significant until we know something about the method of the measurement.

If we know the number of significant figures in 135,000 oz, we can indicate this clearly by using exponential notation to report the measurement number. This is because the digit term in exponential notation contains only significant figures. For example, if we know that a measurement of 135,000 oz has only one significant figure, we can show this clearly by expressing the number as 1×10^5 oz. If a much more exact measurement is made so that 135,000 oz has four significant figures, then we can express the measurement as 1.350×10^5. Thus, an important use of exponential notation is to clearly indicate the number of significant figures in a reported measurement.

C. Rounding Off Numbers

The next few sections explain how significant figures are used in calculations. The general rule about rounding is that **a calculated result can only be as reliable as the least precisely known measurement in the calculation**. This rule makes it necessary to **round off** some numbers, that is, to drop certain digits.

Conventions for rounding off numbers focus on the digit farthest to the right of those that will be kept, the **retained digit**, and the next digit to the right, the **dropped digit**. Thus, if we round off 1.743 to 1.7, the retained digit is 7, and the dropped digit is 4. The following examples show numbers being rounded off to three significant figures.

1. If the dropped digit is less than 5, the retained digit remains unchanged.

For example:

1.634 rounds off to 1.63 (4 is less than 5, so the 3 remains unchanged)

1.6729 rounds off to 1.67 (2 is less than 5, so the 7 remains unchanged)

2. If the dropped digit is a 5 followed by zeros or no digits, the retained digit remains unchanged if it is an even number and is increased by one if it is odd.

For example:

1.635 rounds off to 1.64 (5 with no following digits is dropped, 3 is odd, so the 3 is increased by 1 to 4)

1.625 rounds off to 1.62 (5 with no following digits is dropped, 2 is even, so the 2 remains unchanged)

1.07500 rounds off to 1.08 (5 followed by zeros is dropped, 7 is odd, so the 7 is increased to 8)

3. If the dropped digit is greater than 5 or is a 5 followed by nonzero digits, the retained digit is increased by 1.

For example:

1.637 rounds off to 1.64 (7 is greater than 5, so 3 is increased to 4)

1.647 rounds off to 1.65 (7 is greater than 5, so 4 is increased to 5)

1.48533 rounds off to 1.49 (5 is followed by nonzero digits, so 8 is increased to 9)

D. Rounding Off Calculated Results

In Part C, we noted that a calculated result is only as reliable as the least precisely known measurement in the calculation. We use this rule to determine how many digits to drop when rounding off a calculated result. The type of calculation determines how the rule is applied.

1. Rounding Off in Addition and Subtraction

In addition and subtraction, the least precisely known factor will be the one with the smallest number of decimal places. Therefore, the calculated result must have no more decimal places than the least precisely known number being added or subtracted.

For example, suppose a solution contains 99.6 g of A, 31.62 g of B, and 9.765 g of C. What should be reported as the total mass of the solution? We solve this problem as follows:

mass of A:	99.6 g	→	99.6 g
mass of B:	31.62 g	→	31.6 g
mass of C:	9.765 g	→	9.8 g
total mass:			141.0 g

In other words, we round off all factors until there are no blank spaces in the right-hand column. When using a calculator to do the above addition, we either round off before adding (which requires fewer keystrokes) or we round off the result. In this case, if we use a calculator to add the original numbers, the result is 140.985. We then round off this number to 141.0, which matches the result we obtain when we round off the numbers before adding.

Rounding off in subtraction is done in the same way as in addition. For example, suppose that a beaker containing a solution weighs 72.654 g, while the empty beaker has a mass of 59.6 g. What is the mass of the solution?

mass of beaker and solution:	72.654 g → 72.7 g
mass of beaker:	59.6 g → 59.6 g
mass of solution:	13.1 g

Again, if we use a calculator, we must either round off the result or round off the factors first, as shown.

2. Rounding Off in Multiplication and Division

In multiplication and division, the result can be no more reliable than the least precisely known factor. The least precisely known factor in a multiplication or division problem calculation is simply the factor with the fewest significant figures, regardless of the position of the decimal point. The calculated result must be rounded off so that it contains no more significant figures than does the least precisely known factor.

For example, if we use a calculator to multiply 3.142 times 2.2 we get 6.9124. However, we should not report 6.9124 as our result, because the factor 2.2 contains only two significant figures. Therefore, the reported result can have only two significant figures, so 6.9124 must be rounded off to 6.9.

We can do some rounding off before multiplying or dividing. This will decrease the number of keystrokes needed. First, find the factor with the fewest significant figures. Round off all other factors so they have *one more* significant figure than the least precise factor. The calculated result will be the same as if you used the original factors and then rounded off the result at the end.

For example, consider the density calculation discussed at the beginning of this part of the Procedure:

$$d = \frac{14.3216 \text{ g}}{2.00 \text{ mL}} \quad \begin{array}{l} \longleftarrow \text{(6 significant figures)} \\ \longleftarrow \text{(3 significant figures)} \end{array}$$

Using a calculator, we get the result 7.1608 g/mL, which must be rounded off to 7.16 g/mL (3 significant figures). The reported results, 7.16 g/mL, has the same number of significant figures as does the least precisely known factor, 2.00 mL.

To save keystrokes, we can round off the factors before dividing. In this case, we can round off 14.3216 g

to four significant figures (14.32 g), *one more than* the three significant figures in 2.00 mL. Then we can divide as follows:

$$\frac{14.32 \text{ g}}{2.00 \text{ mL}} = 7.16 \text{ g} / \text{mL}$$

Both methods yield the same result.

E. Significant Figures in Logarithms

Several areas of chemistry use logarithms, which have two parts, the characteristic and the mantissa. The **characteristic** consists of the digits to the left of the decimal point. The **mantissa** consists of the digits to the right of the decimal point. For example, log 2578 = 3.4113. In the logarithm 3.4113, the characteristic is 3 and the mantissa is 4113.

One basic rule governs the number of significant figures that should be reported in a logarithm: **the mantissa of a logarithm should have the same number of significant figures as does the original number.** Some examples are:

log 2 = 0.3 (1 significant figure in 2)

log 2.0 = 0.30 (2 significant figures in 2.0)

log 2.00 = 0.301 (3 significant figures in 2.00)

$\log 2.0 \times 10^4 = 4.30$ (2 significant figures in 2.0)

$\log 2.00 \times 10^{-5} = -4.699$ (3 significant figures in 2.00)

The rule also applies when determining antilogs. Some examples:

antilog 0.48 = 3.0 (2 significant figures in the mantissa)

antilog 0.477 = 3.00 (3 significant figures in the mantissa)

antilog 3.4771 = 3.000×10^3 (4 significant figures in the mantissa)

Problem Set 2

(Use the spaces provided for the answers and additional paper if necessary.)

1. How many significant figures are contained in each of the following numbers?

(a) 0.9463 _____

(b) 0.08206 _____

(c) 6.0225×10^{23} _____

(d) 1.0×10^{-12} _____

(e) 1010 _____

2. Round off each of the following numbers to four significant figures.

(a) 273.15 _____

(b) 12.652 _____

(c) 19.9743 _____

(d) 4.32156 _____

(e) 0.019807 _____

3. Complete the following calculations, and express each result using the proper number of significant figures.

(a) $4.196 + 0.0725 + 14.3 =$

(b) $74.321 - 4.2 =$

(c) $(8.2156 \times 10^2) \times (3.12) =$

(d) $\dfrac{6.042}{7} =$

(e) $\dfrac{0.98 \times 0.230}{0.08206 \times 298} =$

ISBN 0-87540-490-1

4

PROP
602

m o d u l a r · l a b o r a t o r y · p r o g r a m · i n · c h e m i s t r y

publisher: H. A. Neidig
editor: M. L. Gillette

Determining Density

prepared by **M. L. Gillette,** Indiana University Kokomo,
H. A. Neidig, Lebanon Valley College, and **J. N. Spencer,** Franklin and Marshall College

Purpose of the Experiment

Use a balance and graduated cylinders to measure the mass and volume of a liquid and a solid. Using observed mass and volume data, determine the density of rubbing alcohol, a rubber stopper, and an unknown object. Using its calculated density, identify the composition of the unknown object from a list of possibilities.

Background Required

You should understand the terms: volume and mass. You should be familiar with basic laboratory techniques for measuring volumes and masses.

Background Information

When filling out medical forms, we are often asked for our height, weight, and date of birth. Although our height and weight may change from year to year, our date of birth remains constant.

We can distinguish elements and compounds by the properties they possess. Properties that depend on the quantity of the sample are called **extensive** properties. Like our height and weight, the size and mass of a compound vary from sample to sample. In contrast, properties that do not depend on quantity are called **intensive properties**.

For example, as long as the temperature remains constant, the density of a specific compound, like a birth date, is a constant, which makes it an intensive property. We define **density** as the ratio of the mass of a substance to its volume, as shown in Equation 1.

$$\text{density} = \frac{\text{mass}}{\text{volume}} \quad \text{or} \quad d = \frac{m}{V} \qquad \text{(Eq. 1)}$$

The units we use most often to express the density of a liquid are grams per milliliter, or g/mL. For solids, we usually express density in units of grams per cubic centimeter, or g/cm^3. Because 1 mL = 1 cm^3, we can use the density units g/mL and g/cm^3 interchangeably.

We can measure a solid object's mass on a balance, but how can we measure the object's volume? One approach is to find the volume of liquid that the object displaces. To do so, we partially fill a graduated cylinder with a liquid in which the object does not dissolve, which is usually water. We record the exact volume of water in the cylinder. Then we carefully slide the object into the cylinder until it is completely covered with water. The new volume reading represents the combined volume of the water and the object. The difference between these two volumes is the volume of the object.

We follow a similar procedure in order to measure the mass of a liquid. First, we determine the mass of an empty container. Then we add our liquid sample to the container, and reweigh the container plus sample. The difference between these two masses is the sample mass.

We can use density to help identify a substance, but density alone is not enough for a positive identification of its composition. Just as many individuals share the same birth date, many different substances have the same density. In the case of a person, we would need additional information, such as the exact location of birth, to make a positive identification. Similarly, if we know a substance's density and some additional information (such as its melting point, boiling point, or availability in the laboratory), we can usually identify the composition of the substance.

Example

Problem   When a metal sample is placed into a 50-mL graduated cylinder containing 25.0 mL of water, the water level rises to 34.4 mL. The mass of the sample is 67.7 g.

Identify the metal sample as either nickel ($d = 8.90$ g/mL), iron ($d = 7.87$ g/mL), or zinc ($d = 7.13$ g/mL).

Solution   *(1) Determine the volume of the sample.*

metal volume, mL = water plus metal, mL − volume of water, mL
= 34.4 mL − 25.0 mL = 9.4 mL

(2) Calculate the density of the metal sample.

$$d = \frac{m}{v} = \frac{67.7 \text{ g}}{9.4 \text{ mL}} = 7.2 \text{ g / mL}$$

(3) Identify the metal.
The metal must be zinc.

In This Experiment

You will weigh and measure the volume of two rubbing alcohol samples, a rubber stopper, and an unknown object. Using your observed data, you will calculate the densities of the rubbing alcohol, the rubber stopper, and the unknown object. By checking the density of the unknown object against a list of substances and their densities provided by your laboratory instructor, you will identify the composition of your unknown object as one of the substances on the list.

Procedure

Caution: *Wear departmentally approved safety goggles while doing this experiment. Always use caution in the laboratory. Many chemicals are potentially harmful. Prevent contact with your eyes, skin, and clothing. Avoid ingesting any of the reagents.*

Note: • *If you are not familiar with operating the balances that are available in your laboratory, ask your laboratory instructor for assistance*
• *Read and record the volume and mass measurements using the number of figures to the right of the decimal point according to your laboratory instructor's directions*
• *Record all your data on your Data and Observations sheet*

I. Determining the Density of Rubbing Alcohol

Caution: *Rubbing alcohol is a flammable, toxic irritant. Keep it away from open flames and other heat sources. Read the label on the bottle of alcohol provided by your laboratory instructor for additional hazards associated with this substance.*

1. Obtain 10 mL of rubbing alcohol in a dry 50-mL beaker.

If there are several different alcohol solutions available, record the identification code of your sample on your Data and Observations sheet. Otherwise, write "rubbing alcohol" in this space.

2. Weigh a dry, 10-mL graduated cylinder. Record the mass of the cylinder.

3. Remove the cylinder from the balance. Pour 5–6 mL of rubbing alcohol into the cylinder. This portion of alcohol is Sample 1.

Read and record the volume of Sample 1. Be sure to read the bottom of the **meniscus**, or curved liquid surface, as shown in Figure 1.

4. Determine the mass of the graduated cylinder plus Sample 1. Record this mass.

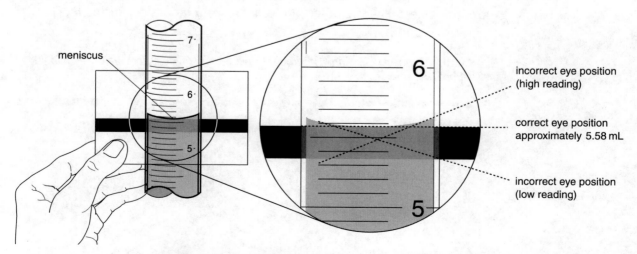

meniscus

6

incorrect eye position (high reading)

correct eye position approximately 5.58 mL

incorrect eye position (low reading)

5

Figure 1 *Using line of sight to correctly read a meniscus*

5. Remove the graduated cylinder from the balance. Add 2–3 mL of rubbing alcohol to Sample 1 in the cylinder. Make sure that the liquid level remains within the calibrated portion of the cylinder. This new volume of alcohol is Sample 2.

Read and record the volume of Sample 2.

6. Determine and record the mass of the graduated cylinder plus Sample 2.

Pour the alcohol in the cylinder into the container labeled "Discarded Rubbing Alcohol". Rinse the cylinder with tap water.

II. Determining the Density of a Rubber Stopper

7. Obtain a dry rubber stopper from your laboratory instructor. Record the identification code of this stopper.

8. Weigh the stopper, and record its mass.

9. Add 50–60 mL of water to a 100-mL graduated cylinder. Read and record the volume of water in the cylinder.

10. With the cylinder slightly tilted, carefully slide the rubber stopper into the water. Avoid splashing any water out of the cylinder. Be sure the stopper is completely submerged.

Read and record the volume of water plus stopper.

11. Pour the water from the cylinder into the sink, taking care not to lose the stopper. Dry the stopper with an absorbent towel. Return it to your laboratory instructor.

III. Determining the Density of an Unknown Object

12. Obtain a dry unknown object from your laboratory instructor. Record the identification code of this object.

13. Weigh the object, and record its mass.

14. Half-fill your 100-mL graduated cylinder with water. Read and record the volume of water in the cylinder.

15. Slightly tilt the graduated cylinder. Carefully slide the object into the water, being careful not to splash any water out of the cylinder. Be sure the object is completely submerged.

Read and record the volume of water plus object.

16. Pour the water from the graduated cylinder into the sink, being careful not to lose the object. Dry the object. Return it to your laboratory instructor.

Caution: *Wash your hands thoroughly with soap or detergent before leaving the laboratory.*

Post-Laboratory Questions

Use the spaces provided for the answers and additional paper if necessary.

1. Compare the densities of your two rubbing alcohol samples.

   (a) Were they identical? If not, why do you think they were different?

   (b) Should these densities have been identical? Briefly explain why or why not.

2. Suppose you had been asked to share your rubber stopper with your laboratory partner. To do this, you cut the stopper into two pieces, and determined the density of your piece. Should you report your experimentally determined density as the density of the stopper, or should you add the density you determined to the one your partner determined, and report this total density? Briefly explain.

3. (a) Suppose that when you added your rubber stopper to the graduated cylinder containing water, some of the water splashed out. Due to this procedural error, would your experimentally determined density of the stopper be erroneously high or erroneously low? Briefly explain.

   (b) Suppose that after a student added his unknown object to the cylinder containing water, the top of the object remained above the surface of the water. After reading the new water level, he calculated the volume of his object. Would his calculated object volume be correct, too high, or too low? Briefly explain.

4. Were the volume measurements you made using the 10-mL graduated cylinder more, less, or equally precise as the volume measurements you made using the 100-mL graduated cylinder? Briefly explain.

5. We said that knowing only the density of a substance is not sufficient to identify it. Yet in this experiment, you identified the composition of a substance by its density. What other information did you have that allowed you to make the identification?

6. The density of water at 0 °C is 0.9999 g/mL, and the density of ice at 0 °C is 0.9168 g/mL.

(a) Based upon these densities, does water contract or expand when it freezes? Briefly explain.

(b) Suppose you have a 250-mL container completely filled with ice. What volume of liquid water will form when the ice melts?

(c) In (b), would water spill out of the container once the ice melted? If so, how much water would spill out? If not, how much water could you add to the container after the ice melted?

Data and Observations

I. Determining the Density of Rubbing Alcohol

identification code of rubbing alcohol   _____

mass of 10-mL graduated cylinder, g   _____

	sample	
	1	2
volume of alcohol sample, mL	_____	_____
mass of 10-mL graduated cylinder and alcohol, g	_____	_____

II. Determining the Density of a Rubber Stopper

identification code of rubber stopper   _____

mass of stopper, g   _____

volume of water, mL   _____

volume of water plus stopper, mL   _____

III. Determining the Density of an Unknown Object

identification code of unknown object   _____

mass of object, g   _____

volume of water, mL   _____

volume of water plus object, mL   _____

Calculations and Conclusions

Show your calculations in the spaces provided. Remember to include units with all calculated results.

I. Determining the Density of Rubbing Alcohol

1. Calculate the mass of each sample, using the mass of the cylinder plus sample and the mass of the cylinder.

mass of Sample 1 _____   mass of Sample 2 _____

2. Calculate the density of each sample, using Equation 1.

density of Sample 1 _____   density of Sample 2 _____

3. Calculate the average density of your rubbing alcohol by adding the densities of Samples 1 and 2, and dividing the sum by 2.

average density of rubbing alcohol _____

identification code of rubbing alcohol _____

II. Determining the Density of a Rubber Stopper

4. Calculate the volume of the rubber stopper, using the volume of the water plus stopper and the volume of the water.

volume of rubber stopper _____

5. Calculate the density of the rubber stopper, using Equation 1.

density of rubber stopper _____

identification code of rubber stopper _____

III. Determining the Density of an Unknown Object

6. Calculate the volume of your unknown object, using a process similar to the one you used in Calculation 4.

volume of unknown object _____

7. Calculate the density of the unknown object, using a process similar to the one you used in Calculation 5.

density of unknown object _____

8. Identify the unknown object. Use the list of substances and their densities supplied by your laboratory instructor to determine the composition of your object. If your experimentally determined density does not match the density of any of the substances on the list, write down the substances whose densities most closely match your experimentally determined density of your unknown.

composition of unknown object _____

identification code of unknown object _____

name partner section date

Pre-Laboratory Assignment

1. What safety precautions should you take when working with rubbing alcohol?

2. Define the following terms as they apply to this experiment:

(a) density

(b) extensive property

3. A student determined the density of an unidentified liquid, known to be one of the following four compounds:

acetone, $d = 0.79$ g/mL

ethyl bromide, $d = 1.46$ g/mL

ethyl chloride, $d = 0.90$ g/mL

ethyl iodide, $d = 1.94$ g/mL

He found that 7.3 mL of the unknown had a mass of 6.52 g.

(a) What is the density of the unknown liquid?

(b) Identify the unknown.

(c) What is the mass of 9.5 mL of ethyl iodide?

(d) What is the volume of an acetone sample whose mass is 6.95 g?

4. A collection of glass beads has a mass of 29.33 g. The beads were transferred to a graduated cylinder containing 13.5 mL of water. The volume of the water plus beads was 25.2 mL. Calculate the density of the glass beads.

ISBN 0-87540-602-5

modular · laboratory · program · in · chemistry
publisher: H. A. Neidig   editor: M. L. Gillette

Resolving a Two-Component Mixture

prepared by **M. L. Gillette**, Indiana University Kokomo;
H. A. Neidig, J. Iskowitz, and **M. Royer**, Lebanon Valley College

Purpose of the Experiment

Separate and recover the components of a mixture of sand and sodium chloride of unknown proportions. Calculate the percent of each component in the mixture and the percent recovery of the components.

Background Required

You should be familiar with basic techniques for measuring volume and mass. You should understand the concepts associated with solution chemistry and stoichiometry.

Background Information

A **binary mixture** is a mixture containing only two components. We can use a variety of methods, either physical or chemical, to separate the components of such a mixture. **Physical separation methods** are based on differences between the physical properties of the components, such as solubility or boiling point.

One physical method for separating a liquid from a solid is **decantation.** First, we allow the solid to settle to the bottom of the container. Then we carefully pour off all of the liquid, called the **supernatant liquid,** or **supernate**, into another container, without disturbing the solid.

We can also physically separate a solid from a liquid by **filtration,** a method that involves pouring the mixture onto a porous material, such as filter paper. The solid, called the **residue,** is unable to pass through the pores in the filter paper, so it is retained on the paper. The liquid, which passes through the paper, is called the **filtrate**.

Evaporation is a third physical separation method, in which a solution is heated to vaporize and thus remove the solvent. The solid remaining after we have evaporated the solvent was the solute.

When one component of a binary mixture of two solids is soluble in a particular solvent, and the other component is not, we can separate the components using a fourth physical method, **extraction**. We add the solvent, dissolving the soluble component, then separate the mixture using filtration.

Example

Problem   Determine the percent recovery of silver bromide (AgBr) and potassium bromide (KBr) when separated from a sample of a binary mixture weighing 2.18 g, according to the following procedure.

Water was added to the mixture with stirring in order to extract the KBr. The remaining solid, AgBr, was collected on a piece of filter paper weighing 0.88 g. When dried, the mass of the paper plus the dry AgBr was 1.82 g. The filtrate was collected in a beaker weighing 69.15 g. After evaporation and cooling, the beaker plus the residue weighed 70.33 g.

Solution

(1) Calculate the mass of AgBr recovered.
The mass of AgBr is equal to the mass of the paper plus AgBr minus the mass of the filter paper.

$$\text{mass of AgBr, g} = 1.82 \text{ g} - 0.88 \text{ g} = 0.94 \text{ g}$$

(2) Calculate the mass of KBr recovered.
The mass of KBr is equal to the mass of the beaker plus KBr minus the mass of the beaker.

$$\text{mass of KBr, g} = 70.33 \text{ g} - 69.15 \text{ g} = 1.18 \text{ g}$$

(3) Calculate the percent AgBr in the mixture.

$$\text{percent AgBr in the mixture, } \% = \left(\frac{\text{mass of AgBr recovered, g}}{\text{mass of sample, g}}\right)(100\%) = \left(\frac{0.94 \text{ g AgBr}}{2.18 \text{ g sample}}\right)(100\%) = 43\%$$

(4) Calculate the percent KBr in the mixture.

$$\text{percent KBr in the mixture, } \% = \left(\frac{1.18 \text{ g KBr}}{2.18 \text{ g sample}}\right)(100\%) = 54\%$$

(5) Calculate your percent recovery of the mixture components.

$$\text{percent recovery, } \% = \left(\frac{\text{total mass of recovered components, g}}{\text{mass of sample, g}}\right)(100\%)$$

$$= \left(\frac{0.94 \text{ g} + 1.18 \text{ g}}{2.18 \text{ g}}\right)(100\%) = \left(\frac{2.12 \text{ g}}{2.18 \text{ g}}\right)(100\%) = 97\%$$

In This Experiment

You will separate and recover sand (silicon dioxide, SiO_2) and table salt (sodium chloride, NaCl) from a binary mixture of unknown proportions, using the procedure outlined in the flowchart in Figure 1 on the next page. After drying and weighing the two recovered compounds, you will calculate the percent of each component in the mixture. You will also calculate your percent recovery of the components.

Procedure

Caution: *Wear departmentally approved safety goggles while doing this experiment. Always use caution in the laboratory. Many chemicals are potentially harmful. Prevent contact with your eyes, skin, and clothing. Avoid ingesting any of the reagents.*

Note:
- *Weigh the portion of mixture you will use for the experiment according to your laboratory instructor's directions.*
- *Record all masses to the nearest centigram (0.01 g).*
- *Dispose of your reaction mixtures and rinses according to your laboratory instructor's directions.*
- *Record all of your data on your Data and Observations sheet.*

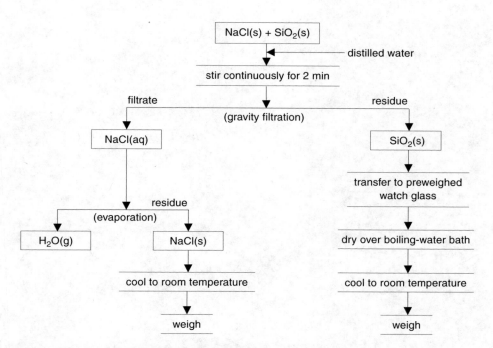

Figure 1 *Flowchart showing the procedure for separating a mixture of NaCl and SiO₂*

I. Preparing the Mixture for Separation

1. Obtain a vial containing your unknown NaCl–SiO$_2$ mixture from your laboratory instructor. Record the identification code of your mixture.

2. Determine the mass of the vial and unknown mixture to the nearest centigram (0.01 g). Record this mass.
Pour the contents of your vial (2–2.5 g) into a dry 150-mL beaker labeled "1". Determine the mass of your empty vial. Record this mass.

II. Separating and Recovering the NaCl

A. Extracting the Mixture with Water

3. Measure 50 mL of distilled or deionized water in a graduated cylinder.
Slowly add the water to the mixture in beaker 1. Stir the mixture while adding the water and for 2 min afterwards.

B. Preparing the Funnel Assembly for Gravity Filtration

4. Place a funnel in a small iron support ring, as shown in Figure 2.

5. Place a piece of filter paper on a dry watch glass. Weigh the glass and paper. Record this mass. Set the watch glass aside for use in Step 16.

> **Note:** *Do not discard the torn-off corner of your filter paper from Step 6. Place it in your paper cone before beginning the filtration.*

6. Fold the filter paper as shown in Figure 3 on the next page. Begin by folding the paper in half (Figure 3b). Make a second fold (Figure 3c), so that the edges of the paper do not quite align (Figure 3d).

Figure 2 *A gravity filtration assembly*

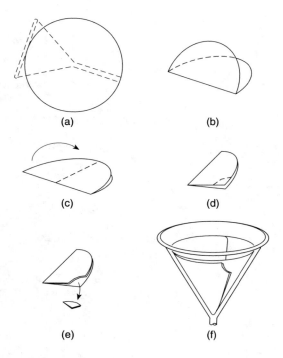

Figure 3 *Folding a piece of filter paper*

Tear off the corner of the smaller section of the paper (Figure 3e). Open up the paper cone and place it in the funnel (Figure 3f). Place the torn-off corner in the paper cone.

7. Label a dry 150-mL beaker "2". Determine the mass of this beaker. Record this mass.

8. Position beaker 2 under the funnel. Make sure the funnel stem touches the inside wall of the beaker (see Figure 2).

9. Moisten the filter paper with distilled water from a wash bottle. Use a stirring rod to firmly press the wet paper against the funnel walls, so that the paper adheres tightly to the funnel.

C. Filtering the Mixture

10. Decant as much of the supernatant liquid as possible from beaker 1 into the funnel. To prevent splashing and possible loss of solid, use a stirring rod to guide the liquid into the funnel, as shown in Figure 4 on the next page. Collect the filtrate in beaker 2.

Transfer the solid remaining in beaker 1 into the funnel, using a stream of distilled water from a wash bottle, as shown in Figure 5 on the next page. Use a rubber policeman to transfer any remaining solid into the funnel.

11. After you have transferred all of the solid, rinse the rubber policeman with a stream of distilled water from the wash bottle. Allow the rinses to go into the funnel and drain into beaker 2.

D. Evaporating the Filtrate

Caution: *In Step 12, as the solution volume decreases, the risk of splattering and sample loss increases. Gentle heating and attentiveness will greatly reduce this risk.*

Figure 4 *Transferring supernatant liquid from a beaker to a filtering funnel*

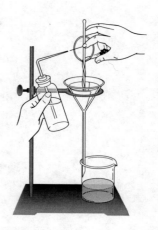

Figure 5 *Transferring solid from a beaker to a filtering funnel*

12. Place beaker 2, containing the filtrate, on a hot plate set on high. Heat the filtrate to boiling.

Slightly reduce the hot plate setting, and allow the solution to boil gently until only 2–3 mL remain.

Adjust the hot plate to its lowest setting, and continue heating the solution until all of the solvent has evaporated.

Caution: *In Step 13, the beaker will be hot. Handle it with beaker tongs.*

13. Turn off the hot plate. Use beaker tongs to remove beaker 2 from the hot plate, as shown in Figure 6.

Note: *You cannot obtain accurate balance readings if you weigh warm objects.*

14. Allow beaker 2 to cool to room temperature. Determine the mass of beaker 2 and its contents. Record this mass.

15. Discard the NaCl into the appropriately labeled container.

Figure 6 *Removing a hot beaker from a hot plate*

III. Recovering SiO$_2$

A. Transferring the SiO$_2$ Residue to a Watch Glass

16. Carefully remove the filter paper and SiO$_2$ residue from the funnel. Place the paper and residue on the watch glass you weighed in Step 5.

Use forceps to unfold and open the filter paper.

B. Drying SiO$_2$

> **Note:** *Your laboratory instructor may ask you to store the watch glass, filter paper, and SiO$_2$ residue in your laboratory bench drawer to dry, and complete the experiment during your next laboratory period.*

> **Caution:** *In Steps 17 and 18, the hot watch glass and the steam coming from beneath the watch glass can burn your hands.*

17. Dry the SiO$_2$ by placing the watch glass over a 400-mL beaker of boiling water on a hot plate, as shown in Figure 7. Continue heating until the SiO$_2$ is completely dry.

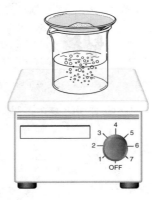

Figure 7 *Drying a solid on a watch glass*

18. Use crucible tongs to move the hot watch glass and its contents to the laboratory bench. Allow the watch glass to cool to room temperature. Carefully dry the bottom of the glass with an absorbent towel.

Determine the mass of the watch glass, filter paper, and SiO$_2$ residue. Record this mass.

19. Discard the SiO$_2$ and filter paper into the appropriately labeled containers.

> **Caution:** *Wash your hands thoroughly with soap or detergent before leaving the laboratory.*

Post-Laboratory Questions

Use the spaces provided for the answers and additional paper if necessary.

1. Consider your percent recovery for this experiment.

   (a) If you recovered less than 100% of your original mixture, which component do you think was more likely lost during the separation? Briefly explain.

   (b) What procedural change would you make to ensure more complete recovery of the lost component you identified in (a)?

   (c) What procedural error(s) could cause a student to report a percent recovery greater than 100%? Briefly explain.

2. Suggest why the procedure you used specified separation of SiO_2 from the NaCl solution by filtration, rather than by decantation.

3. While performing Step 16 of the Procedure, a student accidentally tore the wet filter paper while opening it. How would his results have been affected?

4. You are given a binary mixture of AgCl and lead chloride, $PbCl_2$, of unknown proportions. Both compounds are insoluble in cold water, and only $PbCl_2$ is soluble in hot water.

(a) Devise a method for separating the two components.

(b) Draw a flowchart illustrating your separation scheme.

(c) After completing the separation, you learn that your calculated percent recovery of one of the components is low. For which component was your recovery probably low? Briefly explain.

name _____   partner _____   section _____   date _____

Data and Observations

identification code of unknown _____

mass of vial plus sample, g _____

mass of empty vial, g _____

mass of beaker 2, g _____

mass of beaker 2 plus NaCl, g _____

mass of watch glass and filter paper, g _____

mass of watch glass, filter paper, and SiO_2, g _____

Calculations and Conclusions

Show your calculations in the space provided. Remember to include units with all calculated results.

1. Calculate the mass of unknown mixture that you analyzed.

mass of unknown _____

2. Calculate the mass of NaCl recovered.

mass of NaCl _____

3. Calculate the mass of SiO_2 recovered.

mass of SiO_2 _____

4. Calculate the percent NaCl in your unknown mixture.

percent NaCl _____

5. Calculate the percent SiO_2 in your unknown mixture.

percent SiO_2 _____

6. Calculate the total mass of NaCl and SiO_2 recovered.

total mass recovered _____

7. Calculate your percent recovery of the components.

percent recovery _____

Pre-Laboratory Assignment

1. What hazards should you be aware of when evaporating a solvent from a solution?

2. Distinguish between the following pairs of terms, as they apply to this experiment:

(a) decantation and filtration

(b) supernate and filtrate

(c) evaporation and extraction

3. Regarding the techniques you will use in this experiment, briefly explain:

(a) why you must place the torn-off corner of filter paper into the paper cone (Step 6).

(b) why you must allow an object to cool to room temperature before you determine its mass.

4. Draw a flowchart for the **Example** separation in the Background Information.

ISBN 0-87540-603-3

REAC
604

modular · laboratory · program · in · chemistry

publisher: H. A. Neidig   editor: M. L. Gillette

Observing Signs of Chemical Reaction

prepared by **M. L. Gillette**, Indiana University Kokomo,
and **H. A. Neidig**, Lebanon Valley College

Purpose of the Experiment

Observe and record the physical characteristics of solids and solutions. Observe and record changes that occur when the solids and solutions are mixed and react chemically.

Background Required

You should be familiar with basic laboratory techniques for transferring liquids and solids.

Background Information

Chemists study the behavior of atoms, ions, molecules, and compounds, and the transformations these substances undergo. There are two general types of transformations that occur: physical and chemical.

Physical changes, such as melting or boiling, do not alter the chemical composition of the substance. For example, when we warm ice (solid water, H_2O) to 32 °F (0 °C), it melts, forming liquid water (H_2O). If we continue heating the liquid water until it reaches 212 °F (100 °C), it will boil, forming steam, which is H_2O vapor. Thus, while the physical state of the water changes during this process, its chemical composition, H_2O, does not.

In contrast to physical changes, **chemical changes** do alter the chemical composition of the substance through a chemical reaction. Signs that a chemical change has occurred include the following:

1. **Formation of a precipitate** when two solutions are mixed. The **precipitate**, a substance that is insoluble in the reaction mixture, may either settle to the bottom of the solution container or it may form a suspension in the reaction mixture.

2. A **color change** that represents more than just a change in physical state or the dilution of one solution by another. The interactions of some substances with visible light make them appear colored, so the color of a substance may change when its chemical composition changes.

3. **Evolution of a gas** from the reaction mixture. The gas may or may not have a detectable odor or color. When a reaction product is a gas that is insoluble in

the reaction mixture, the gas will bubble out of the mixture. If the gas is soluble in the reaction mixture, its formation will not be visually evident.

4. A **temperature change** in the reaction mixture not caused by external heating or cooling. Every chemical reaction involves an energy change. This change may cause either an increase or decrease in the reaction mixture temperature.

In This Experiment

You will carry out nine chemical reactions. For each reaction, based on your detailed observations of the reactants and products, you will identify evidence proving that a chemical change has occurred.

Procedure

Caution: *Wear departmentally approved safety goggles while doing this experiment. Always use caution in the laboratory. Many chemicals are potentially harmful. Prevent contact with your eyes, skin, and clothing. Avoid ingesting any of the reagents.*

Note: • *Dispose of your reaction mixtures and rinses according to your laboratory instructor's directions.*
• *Record all of your data on your Data and Observations sheet. Include detailed descriptions of your reagents before you combine them, and careful observations of your reaction mixtures. Be sure to record any color change, precipitate formation, or gas evolution.*

I. Performing the Reactions

Table 1 shows the nine different combinations of reagents you will observe and mix. Record all observations on the appropriate lines of your Data and Observations sheet as you proceed.

Table 1 *Reagent Combinations*

mixture letter	start with this reagent	add this reagent
A	95% ethyl alcohol	cobalt(II) chloride hexahydrate ($CoCl_2 \cdot 6H_2O$)
B	mixture A	distilled water
C	mixture B	0.5M sodium hydrogen carbonate ($NaHCO_3$)
D	1M hydrochloric acid (HCl)	magnesium (Mg)
E	0.1M copper(II) sulfate ($CuSO_4$)	steel wool
F	0.1M $CuSO_4$	0.5M $NaHCO_3$
G	mixture F	1M ammonia (NH_3)
H	1M HCl	$NaHCO_3$
I	barium hydroxide octahydrate ($Ba(OH)_2 \cdot 8H_2O$)	ammonium thiocyanate (NH_4SCN)

A. Adding $CoCl_2 \cdot 6H_2O$ to 95% Ethyl Alcohol

> **Caution:** *Cobalt(II) chloride hexahydrate is toxic and irritating. Ethyl alcohol is flammable and toxic.*

> **Note:** *The success of this reaction depends on your beginning with a **dry** test tube.*

1. Place 6 clean, **dry**, 13×100-mm test tubes in a support rack. Label the tubes 1–6.

2. From your laboratory instructor, obtain 2 mL of 95% ethyl alcohol and the amount of $CoCl_2 \cdot 6H_2O$ crystals needed to fill the end of a microspatula. Record descriptions of your reagents on your Data and Observations sheet.

3. Combine the two reagents in test tube 1. Stir the reaction mixture with a clean glass stirring rod. Observe the reaction mixture, looking for any signs of change. Record your observations on your Data and Observations sheet.

4. Save this mixture for use in reaction **B**.

B. Adding Distilled Water to the $CoCl_2 \cdot 6H_2O$–95% Ethyl Alcohol Mixture

5. Repeat Step 3, combining the $CoCl_2 \cdot 6H_2O$–95% ethyl alcohol mixture from reaction *A* with 1 mL of distilled or deionized water. Be sure to record the appearance of the water before you add it.

6. Save this mixture for use in reaction *C*.

C. Adding 0.5M $NaHCO_3$ to the $CoCl_2 \cdot 6H_2O$–95% Ethyl Alcohol–Water Mixture

7. Repeat Step 3, combining the $CoCl_2 \cdot 6H_2O$–95% ethyl alcohol–water mixture from reaction *B* with 1 mL of 0.5*M* $NaHCO_3$. Be sure to record the appearance of the $NaHCO_3$ before you add it.

8. Pour the mixture into the appropriate container provided by your laboratory instructor. Rinse the test tube and stirring rod with tap water, and then with distilled water. Allow the test tube to drain.

D. Adding Mg to 1M HCl

> **Caution:** *1M HCl is toxic and corrosive. Mg is flammable and moisture-sensitive.*

9. Using test tube 2, repeat Steps 2 and 3, this time combining 2 mL of 1*M* HCl and a 1-cm piece of Mg ribbon.

10. Pour the mixture into the appropriately labeled container provided by your laboratory instructor. Rinse the test tube and stirring rod as described in Step 8.

E. Adding Steel Wool to 0.1M $CuSO_4$

> **Caution:** *0.1M Copper(II) sulfate is toxic and irritating.*

11. Using test tube 3, repeat Steps 2 and 3, this time combining 2 mL of 0.1*M* $CuSO_4$ and a small wad (1.5-cm diameter) of steel wool.

12. Pour the mixture into the appropriate container provided by your laboratory instructor. Rinse the test tube and stirring rod as described in Step 8.

F. Adding 0.5M NaHCO₃ to 0.1M CuSO₄

13. Using test tube 4, repeat Steps 2 and 3, this time combining 2 mL of $0.1M$ $CuSO_4$ and 1 mL of $0.5M$ $NaHCO_3$.

14. Save the mixture for use in reaction G.

G. Adding 1M NH₃ to the CuSO₄–NaHCO₃ Mixture

Caution: $1M$ NH_3 is corrosive.

15. In a **fume hood**, repeat Step 3, combining the $CuSO_4$–$NaHCO_3$ mixture from reaction F with 2 mL of $1M$ NH_3. Be sure to record the appearance of the NH_3 solution before you add it.

16. Pour the mixture into the appropriate container provided by your laboratory instructor. Rinse the test tube and stirring rod as described in Step 8.

H. Adding NaHCO₃ to 1M HCl

17. Using test tube 5, repeat Steps 2 and 3, this time combining 2 mL of $1M$ HCl with the amount of $NaHCO_3$ needed to fill the end of your microspatula.

18. Pour the mixture into the appropriate container provided by your laboratory instructor. Rinse the test tube and stirring rod as described in Step 8.

I. Adding NH₄SCN to Ba(OH)₂ · 8H₂O

Caution: $Ba(OH)_2 \cdot 8H_2O$ is toxic and corrosive. NH_4SCN is toxic and irritating.

19. Using test tube 6, repeat steps 2 and 3, combining the amount of $Ba(OH)_2 \cdot 8H_2O$ needed to fill the end of your microspatula and a slightly smaller quantity of NH_4SCN. Cautiously note any odor associated with the reaction mixture.

20. Pour the mixture into the appropriate container provided by your laboratory instructor. Rinse the test tube and stirring rod as described in Step 8.

II. Drawing Conclusions from Your Observations, and Cleaning Up

21. For each reaction (A–I), list the evidence proving that a chemical change occurred. Check your evidence with your laboratory instructor. Your laboratory instructor may ask you to repeat one or more of the reactions, if your observations are not complete.

22. Wash your test tubes with soap or detergent. Rinse the tubes with tap water, then distilled water.

Caution: *Wash your hands thoroughly with soap or detergent before leaving the laboratory.*

Post-Laboratory Questions

Use the spaces provided for the answers and additional paper if necessary.

1. Explain why it was essential that you began reaction *A* with a dry test tube.

2. Throughout the Procedure, you observed each reaction mixture to determine whether or not a chemical change occurred. The Background Information lists four possible signs indicating a chemical change. Suggest an adjustment to the Procedure that would allow you to detect a sign of chemical change that you did not observe during the current Procedure.

3. A student performing an experiment similar to the one described in the Procedure combined a clear, red solution with a clear, yellow–brown solution. The resulting solution was clear and orange. From this evidence, can the student conclude that a chemical change took place? Briefly explain.

4. A student placed a blue solid into a test tube and heated the tube. The solid turned white, and droplets of clear, colorless liquid collected on the inner test tube wall, near the top of the tube. Did the student observe a physical or a chemical change? Briefly explain.

Data and Observations

I. Performing the Reactions

A. Adding $CoCl_2 \cdot 6H_2O$ to 95% Ethyl Alcohol

reagents	appearance of reagents	appearance of mixture A
95% ethyl alcohol		
$CoCl_2 \cdot 6H_2O$		
evidence of a chemical reaction:		

B. Adding Distilled Water to the $CoCl_2 \cdot 6H_2O$–95% Ethyl Alcohol Mixture

reagents	appearance of reagents	appearance of mixture B
mixture A		
distilled water		
evidence of a chemical reaction:		

C. Adding 0.5M $NaHCO_3$ to the $CoCl_2 \cdot 6H_2O$–95% Ethyl Alcohol–Water Mixture

reagents	appearance of reagents	appearance of mixture C
mixture B		
0.5M $NaHCO_3$		
evidence of a chemical reaction:		

D. Adding Mg to 1M HCl

reagents	appearance of reagents	appearance of mixture D
1M HCl		
Mg		
evidence of a chemical reaction:		

E. Adding Steel Wool to 0.1M CuSO$_4$

reagents	appearance of reagents	appearance of mixture E
0.1M CuSO$_4$		
steel wool		
evidence of a chemical reaction:		

F. Adding 0.5M NaHCO$_3$ to 0.1M CuSO$_4$

reagents	appearance of reagents	appearance of mixture F
0.1M CuSO$_4$		
0.5M NaHCO$_3$		
evidence of a chemical reaction:		

name   partner   section   date

G. Adding 1M NH₃ to the CuSO₄–NaHCO₃ Mixture

reagents	appearance of reagents	appearance of mixture G
mixture *F*		
1*M* NH₃		
evidence of a chemical reaction:		

H. Adding NaHCO₃ to 1M HCl

reagents	appearance of reagents	appearance of mixture H
1*M* HCl		
NaHCO₃		
evidence of a chemical reaction:		

I. Adding NH₄SCN to Ba(OH)₂ · 8H₂O

reagents	appearance of reagents	appearance of mixture I
Ba(OH)₂ · 8H₂O		
NH₄SCN		
evidence of a chemical reaction:		

name partner section date

Pre-Laboratory Assignment

1. What hazards should you be aware of when working with the following substances?

   (a) 1*M* NH_3

   (b) 1*M* HCl

2. Briefly explain the difference between a physical change and a chemical change.

3. Describe what you will observe if:

   (a) a precipitate forms when you mix two solutions?

   (b) a gas is released from the reaction mixture?

   (c) a colored component dissolves in water and reacts to form a colorless product?

ISBN 0-87540-604-1

modular · laboratory · program · in · chemistry

publisher: H. A. Neidig

editor: M. L. Gillette

Determining the Percent Water in an Unknown Hydrate

prepared by **M. L. Gillette**, Indiana University Kokomo; **H. A. Neidig**, Lebanon Valley College; and **J. N. Spencer**, Franklin and Marshall College

Purpose of the Experiment

Determine the percent water in an unknown hydrate.

Background Required

You should be familiar with basic laboratory techniques for measuring mass and using a Bunsen burner. You should understand the concepts associated with stoichiometry.

Background Information

Many solid ionic compounds contain weakly bound water molecules within their crystal structures. We call such solids **hydrates** and the bound water molecules we call **water(s) of hydration.** We include the water(s) of hydration in the name and chemical formula for a hydrate, connecting the water(s) to the rest of the formula with a raised dot. For example, the chemical formula for copper(II) sulfate pentahydrate is $CuSO_4 \cdot 5H_2O$.

We can remove the water(s) of hydration from a hydrate using a process called **dehydration,** leaving the **anhydrous** ("without water") form of the compound. We usually dehydrate compounds by heating them. For example, when we heat blue $CuSO_4 \cdot 5H_2O$, the waters of hydration are released as water vapor, and solid, white anhydrous $CuSO_4$ remains, as shown in Equation 1.

$$CuSO_4 \cdot 5H_2O(s, \text{blue}) \xrightarrow{\text{heat}} CuSO_4(s, \text{white}) + 5\,H_2O(g) \quad \text{(Eq. 1)}$$

Example

Problem

The mass of a clean, dry crucible is 10.427 g. The mass of the crucible after the addition of a sample of unknown green hydrate is 12.179 g. After heating, the crucible plus solid yellow residue weighs 11.459 g. Determine the percent water in the unknown hydrate.

Solution

(a) *Calculate the mass of hydrate heated.*

$$12.179 \text{ g} - 10.427 \text{ g} = 1.752 \text{ g}$$

(b) *Calculate the mass of water in the hydrate sample.*

$$12.179 \text{ g} - 11.459 \text{ g} = 0.720 \text{ g}$$

(c) Calculate the percent water in the hydrate sample, using Equation 2.

$$\text{percent water, } \% = \left(\frac{\text{mass of water lost, g}}{\text{mass of hydrate heated, g}} \right)(100\%) = \left(\frac{0.720 \text{ g}}{1.752 \text{ g}} \right)(100\%) = 41.1\% \quad \text{(Eq. 2)}$$

In This Experiment

You will determine the mass of a hydrated salt sample and the mass of the residue after heating the sample. From these masses, you will calculate the mass of water lost during heating and the percent water in the hydrate.

Procedure

Caution: *Wear departmentally approved safety goggles while doing this experiment. Always use caution in the laboratory. Many chemicals are potentially harmful. Prevent contact with your eyes, skin, and clothing. Avoid ingesting any of the reagents. Use care when handling hot objects.*

Note:
- *Clean your crucible according to your laboratory instructor's directions.*
- *Always use crucible tongs to handle the crucible and its cover, in order to avoid contaminating the crucible and cover with finger oils and to prevent burns from the hot crucible.*
- *If you need assistance, either in adjusting your Bunsen burner to obtain a nonluminous flame, or in heating your sample both gently and strongly, consult your laboratory instructor.*
- *Record all masses to either the nearest milligram (0.001 g) or nearest centigram (0.01 g), as indicated by your laboratory instructor.*
- *Record all data on your Data and Observations sheet.*
- *If you perform a second determination, obtain a second clean, dry crucible and cover for that determination.*
- *Dispose of your reaction mixtures according to your laboratory instructor's directions.*

I. Preparing and Weighing the Crucible

1. Obtain an unknown hydrate sample from your laboratory instructor. Record the identification code of your hydrate.

2. Attach a support ring to a ring stand. Place a pipe-stem triangle on the ring. Using crucible tongs, place a clean, dry porcelain crucible on the triangle.

Place a ceramic-centered wire gauze on the laboratory bench, beside the support stand.

3. Gently heat the crucible for 5 min, using a nonluminous Bunsen burner flame.

Extinguish the burner flame. Using the tongs, move the hot crucible from the triangle to the wire gauze to cool.

Note: *In order to accurately determine the mass of an object, be sure that the object is at room temperature.*

II. Heating and Weighing the Unknown Hydrate

4. When you feel no heat when holding your hand 1–2 cm from the crucible, weigh it. Record this mass. Leave the crucible on the balance pan.

5. With the crucible still on the balance pan, use a microspatula to transfer a small amount of your hydrate into the crucible. Continue adding small amounts of your hydrate, until the mass of the crucible plus hydrate is about 2 g more than the mass of the crucible alone.

Record the exact total mass of the crucible and hydrate.

6. Using the tongs, place the crucible and contents at a slight angle in the triangle, as shown in Figure 1. Place a cover on the crucible as shown in Figure 1, leaving it ajar to allow water vapor from the heated hydrate to escape. The cover will help prevent loss of material in case of splattering.

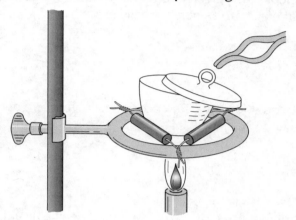

Figure 1 *Heating a crucible and cover*

7. *Gently* heat the cover, crucible, and contents for 5 min, using a nonluminous Bunsen burner flame. Strong heating will cause splattering.

After 5 min, position the burner so that the inner cone of the flame contacts the lower edge of the crucible bottom. Heat the crucible more strongly, until the bottom turns slightly red. Then continue strong heating for 10 min more.

8. After 10 min, extinguish the burner flame. Allow the crucible and cover to cool for 5−10 min in the triangle.

9. Using the tongs, remove the cover, and then the crucible and its contents, from the triangle. Place them on the wire gauze to finish cooling.

10. When the crucible has cooled to room temperature (see Step 4), use the tongs to transfer the crucible and its contents to the balance. Weigh the crucible and its contents. Record this total mass.

11. Discard the crucible contents into the appropriately labeled container provided by your laboratory instructor.

Thoroughly wash the microspatula, crucible, and cover. Rinse them with tap water, then with distilled water.

12. If time permits, do a second determination, repeating Steps 2−11.

13. From your laboratory instructor, obtain either the chemical formula or the actual percent water of your unknown hydrate. Record this information.

Caution: *Wash your hands thoroughly with soap or detergent before leaving the laboratory.*

Post-Laboratory Questions

Use the spaces provided for the answers and additional paper if necessary.

1. If you performed two determinations, use your results to answer the following questions.

   (a) Is your calculated percent water in the hydrate the same for both determinations?

   (b) Should the percent water be the same for both determinations, even though you started with two different-size samples? Briefly explain.

   (c) Account for any difference between your two determinations.

2. If your laboratory instructor gave you the chemical formula for your unknown hydrate, answer (a) and (b). If your instructor gave you the actual percent water in your hydrate, answer (b) only.

   (a) Calculate the theoretical percent water in your hydrate.

   (b) Calculate the percent error in your average determination, using Equation 3.

$$\text{percent error, \%} = \left(\frac{\begin{array}{c}\text{average experimental percent} \\ \text{water in hydrate, \%}\end{array} - \begin{array}{c}\text{theoretical percent} \\ \text{water in hydrate, \%}\end{array}}{\begin{array}{c}\text{theoretical percent water} \\ \text{in hydrate, \%}\end{array}} \right)(100\%) \qquad \text{(Eq. 3)}$$

3. (a) Why was it important to heat your hydrate gently for 5 min, before heating it strongly for 10 min?

   (b) Based upon your answer to (a), what was the purpose of the crucible cover in this experiment?

name ____________ partner ____________ section ____________ date ____________

Data and Observations

II. Heating and Weighing the Unknown Hydrate

identification code of unknown hydrate ____________

	determination 1	2
mass of crucible, g	____________	____________
initial mass of crucible and hydrate, g	____________	____________
mass of crucible and dehydrated compound, g	____________	____________

chemical formula of unknown hydrate
(as obtained from laboratory instructor) ____________

actual percent water in unknown hydrate, %
(as obtained from laboratory instructor) ____________

Calculations and Conclusions

Show your calculations in the space provided. Remember to include units with all calculated results.

1. Calculate the mass of hydrate heated.

sample 1 ____________ sample 2 ____________

2. Calculate the mass of water lost from the hydrate during heating.

sample 1 _____   sample 2 _____

3. Calculate the percent water in the hydrate, using Equation 2.

sample 1 _____   sample 2 _____

4. If you performed two determinations, calculate the average percent water in your hydrate.

average percent water in the hydrate _____

Pre-Laboratory Assignment

1. (a) State two reasons why you should always use crucible tongs to handle the crucible in this experiment.

    (b) How will you determine that your crucible has returned to room temperature after heating?

    (c) Why is it important to allow your crucible to cool to room temperature before weighing it?

2. (a) What do we mean by the phrase "water(s) of hydration"?

    (b) Briefly describe the difference between a hydrate and its anhydrous form.

3. A student followed the Procedure of this experiment, using her unknown hydrate, and obtained the following data.

mass of crucible, g	10.439
mass of crucible and hydrate, g	11.844
mass of crucible and dehydrated sample, g	11.213

(a) Calculate the mass of hydrate heated.

(b) Calculate the mass of water in the hydrate.

(c) Calculate the percent water in the hydrate.

ISBN 0-87540-605-X

modular · laboratory · program · in · chemistry

publisher: H. A. Neidig   editor: M. L. Gillette

Determining the Empirical Formula of Magnesium Oxide

prepared by **M. L. Gillette**, Indiana University Kokomo;
H. A. Neidig, Lebanon Valley College; and **J. N. Spencer**, Franklin and Marshall College

Purpose of the Experiment

Determine the empirical formula of magnesium oxide.

Background Required

You should be familiar with basic laboratory techniques for measuring mass and using a Bunsen burner, and the concepts associated with chemical formulas, molar mass, and ionic compounds.

Background Information

To understand the behavior of a chemical compound we must first know its chemical formula. The simplest molar combining ratio of the elements in a compound is called the **empirical formula.** We can determine the ratio if we know the mass of the individual elements in a known mass of the compound. For most ionic compounds, compounds formed from metals and nonmetals, the empirical formula is the same as the compound formula. For covalent compounds, compounds formed from nonmetals, the empirical formula is not necessarily the same as the molecular formula of the compound. For example, the empirical formula of water, H_2O, is the same as its molecular formula. In contrast, the empirical formula of hydrogen peroxide is HO, but its molecular formula is H_2O_2. To determine whether or not a covalent compound's empirical and molecular formulas are the same, we need to know the molar mass of the compound.

We can form an oxide of a metal by heating the metal in air. If we know the mass of metal heated and the mass of metal oxide formed, we can determine the empirical formula of the metal oxide produced.

Example

Problem   Determine the empirical formula of an oxide of titanium (Ti). A 3.45-g Ti sample is heated in an open vessel to produce a compound containing Ti and oxygen (O), Ti_xO_y. The mass of the product is 5.76 g.

Solution   *(1) Calculate the mass of O that combined with the Ti.*

mass of O, g = mass of oxide, g − mass of metal, g

= 5.76 g − 3.45 g = 2.31 g O

(2) Calculate the number of moles of Ti that reacted. The molar mass of Ti is 47.9 g/mol.

$$\text{number of moles of Ti, mol} = (\text{mass of Ti, g}) \left(\frac{1 \text{ mol Ti}}{47.9 \text{ g Ti}}\right) = (3.45 \text{ g Ti}) \left(\frac{1 \text{ mol Ti}}{47.9 \text{ g Ti}}\right) = 7.20 \times 10^{-2} \text{ mol Ti}$$

(3) Calculate the number of moles of O that combined with 7.20×10^{-2} mol of Ti. The molar mass of O is 16.0 g/mol.

$$\text{number of moles of O, mol} = (\text{mass of O, g}) \left(\frac{1 \text{ mol O}}{16.0 \text{ g O}}\right) = (2.31 \text{ g O}) \left(\frac{1 \text{ mol O}}{16.0 \text{ g O}}\right) = 0.144 \text{ mol O}$$

(4) Find the simplest ratio of the number of moles of Ti to the number of moles of O. Divide the number of moles of Ti and of O by the smaller of the two molar amounts, in this case, the number of moles of Ti.

$$\frac{7.20 \times 10^{-2} \text{ mol Ti}}{7.20 \times 10^{-2}} = 1 \text{ mol Ti}$$

$$\frac{0.144 \text{ mol O}}{7.20 \times 10^{-2}} = 2 \text{ mol O}$$

(5) Write the empirical formula for titanium oxide.
$Ti_1 O_2$, or TiO_2

In This Experiment

You will heat a measured mass of magnesium (Mg) in an open crucible to form a compound containing Mg and O. You will use the masses of the Mg and of the product to calculate the mass of O in the product. Finally, you will determine the empirical formula of the product, magnesium oxide.

Procedure

> **Caution:** *Wear departmentally approved safety goggles while doing this experiment. Always use caution in the laboratory. Many chemicals are potentially harmful. Prevent contact with your eyes, skin, and clothing. Avoid ingesting any of the reagents. Use care when handling objects that become hot during laboratory procedures.*

Note: • *Record sample masses to the nearest milligram (0.001 g) or to the nearest centigram (0.01 g), according to your laboratory instructor's directions.*
• *Record all of your data on your Data and Observations sheet.*

I. Preparing and Weighing the Crucible and Cover

1. Attach an iron ring to a support stand. Allow sufficient height to place a Bunsen burner beneath the ring, as shown in Figure 1 on the next page.

Place ceramic-centered wire gauze on the bench beside the support stand.

Note: *Throughout the procedure, use crucible tongs to handle the crucible and its cover. This technique will help to protect your hands from burns. Also, oils and other contaminants will be prevented from being transferred to the crucible.*

2. Place a clay or Nichrome triangle on the ring. Place a clean, dry porcelain crucible at a slight angle on the triangle, as shown in Figure 1. Balance a crucible cover on the open crucible, as shown in Figure 2.

3. Light the Bunsen burner and adjust the gas/air mixture to give a nonluminous flame.

4. Gently heat the crucible for 5 min.

5. Turn off the burner. Place the hot crucible cover on the wire gauze to cool. Then, move the hot crucible from the triangle to the wire gauze to cool.

Note: *An object must be at room temperature for its mass to be accurately determined on a balance.*

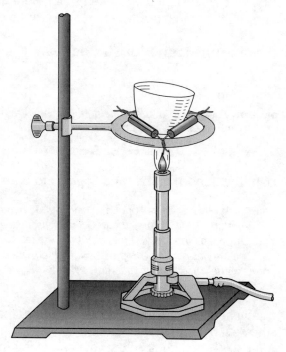

Figure 1 *Apparatus for determination of empirical formula*

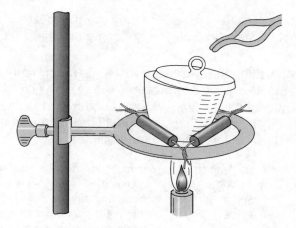

Figure 2 *Position of crucible cover for heating*

6. When you feel no heat as you hold your hand 1–2 cm from the crucible, transfer the crucible and cover to your balance. Determine and record the mass of the crucible and cover.

II. Preparing the Magnesium for Reaction

> **Note:** *If your magnesium appears to have a white oxide coating on it, clean it with sandpaper before proceeding with Step 7.*

7. Obtain an untarnished piece of magnesium ribbon weighing 0.3–0.5 g from your laboratory instructor. Loosely roll the magnesium ribbon into a ball and place it in the crucible.

8. Place the crucible, Mg, and cover on the balance and determine their combined mass. Record this mass.

9. Place the crucible and its contents at a slight angle on the triangle, as shown in Figure 1. Place the crucible cover on the open crucible as shown in Figure 2.

III. Producing Magnesium Oxide

> **Caution:** *The light from the white flame of the burning magnesium can damage your eyes. Never look directly into this flame.*

10. Light the Bunsen burner and adjust it to obtain a nonluminous flame.

> **Note:** *White smoke will appear while you are heating the crucible. This smoke is magnesium oxide. To prevent loss of your product, you should **completely** cover the crucible as soon as you see the white smoke.*
> *The Mg has reacted completely when there are no signs of smoke and the contents of the crucible no longer glow brightly.*

11. Gently heat the crucible. As soon as white smoke appears, close the crucible with the cover. Remove the flame.
After 10–15 s, slightly lift the cover and look for white smoke. If smoke is evident, proceed to Step 12. If there is no smoke, proceed to Step 13.

12. Repeat the processes of uncovering, heating, and covering the crucible (repeating Step 11) until you no longer observe white smoke.

13. Position the crucible cover as shown in Figure 2. Position the Bunsen burner so that the flame contacts the bottom of the crucible (see Figure 2). Apply strong heat until the crucible bottom is slightly red. Continue to strongly heat the crucible for 10 min. The crucible should be slightly red throughout the 10-min period.
Turn off the Bunsen burner flame.

> **Note:** *Magnesium also reacts with atmospheric nitrogen (N_2) to form magnesium nitride (Mg_3N_2). Mg_3N_2 is converted to magnesium oxide when it reacts with water. Be careful in Step 14 not to lose any of the white, fluffy solid in the crucible.*
> *Before adding water in Step 14, allow the crucible to cool to room temperature. If the crucible is not cool, it may crack when water is added and you will have to begin the procedure again.*

Handle the crucible cover carefully. To cool it, invert the cover on the wire gauze during cooling in Steps 14 and 16. A small amount of product will probably have collected on the cover.

14. Remove the crucible cover, invert it, and place it on the wire gauze to cool. Allow the crucible to remain on the triangle to cool. When the crucible reaches room temperature, use a medicine dropper or Beral pipet to add 10 drops of distilled or deionized water to the crucible.

Replace the cover on the crucible, leaving it slightly ajar, as shown in Figure 2.

> **Note:** *In Step 15, you will heat the crucible to evaporate the excess water. Do not overheat the crucible. Excessive heating will cause spattering, resulting in loss of magnesium oxide from the crucible.*

15. Light the Bunsen burner and adjust it to obtain a nonluminous flame. Gently heat the crucible for 5 min. Then heat the crucible strongly to red heat for 5 min. Turn off the Bunsen burner.

16. Remove the cover, invert it, and place it on the wire gauze to cool. Then remove the crucible from the triangle and place it on the wire gauze to cool.

17. When the crucible is cool, transfer the crucible and the cover to the balance. Weigh the crucible, its contents, and the cover. Record this mass.

18. Discard the magnesium oxide into the Discarded Magnesium Oxide container.

Thoroughly wash the crucible and its cover with tap water. Rinse them with distilled water. Dry them with a disposable towel.

> **Note:** *If your laboratory instructor indicates that there is sufficient time to repeat the experiment, use a clean, dry crucible for the second determination.*

19. If time permits, do a second determination.

Caution: *Wash your hands thoroughly with soap or detergent before leaving the laboratory.*

name   partner   section   date

Post-Laboratory Questions

Use the spaces provided for the answers and additional paper if necessary.

1. If you performed two determinations, compare the results of these experiments.

    (a) Would you expect the empirical formula you determined for magnesium oxide to be the same as the one determined by another student?

    (b) Would you expect an empirical formula to be the same even though different masses of Mg were used? Briefly explain.

    (c) If different masses of Mg are used, account for any difference in the empirical formulas.

2. A student performed this experiment using magnesium that had a dull, white coating.

    (a) What was the probable identity of the dull coating?

    (b) What effect would the presence of this coating have on the experimentally determined mass of magnesium in magnesium oxide? Briefly explain.

3. When a student removed the crucible cover after the first strong heating (Step 13), some of the white solid was knocked from the cover to the floor and lost. Did this loss cause the calculated number of moles of oxygen in the compound to be too high or too low? Briefly explain.

4. A student wanting to leave the laboratory early weighed the cooled crucible from Step 13 and used this mass as the mass of the crucible, cover, and magnesium oxide. Would this produce a calculated number of moles of oxygen in magnesium oxide that is too high or too low? Briefly explain.

5. A student found that 1.19 g of chromium (Cr) formed 1.74 g of chromium oxide. The molar mass of Cr is 52.00 g/mol. What is the empirical formula of chromium oxide?

name   partner   section   date

Data and Observations

	determination	
	1	*2*
mass of crucible and cover, g	_____	_____
mass of crucible, cover, and Mg, g	_____	_____
mass of crucible, cover, and magnesium oxide, g	_____	_____

Calculations and Conclusions

Show your calculations in the spaces provided. Remember to include units with all calculated results.

III. Producing Magnesium Oxide

1. Calculate the mass of Mg reacted.

determination 1 _____   determination 2 _____

2. Calculate the mass of magnesium oxide formed.

determination 1 _____   determination 2 _____

3. Calculate the mass of O that combined with the Mg.

determination 1 _____   determination 2 _____

4. Calculate the average number of moles of Mg that reacted. The molar mass of Mg is 24.31 g/mol.

average number of moles of Mg _____

5. Calculate the average number of moles of O that combined with the Mg. The molar mass of O is 16.00 g/mol.

average number of moles of O _____

6. Find the simplest ratio of the average number of moles of Mg to the average number of moles of O.

(a) Divide the average number of moles of Mg by the smaller of the average numbers of moles of Mg or of O.

(b) Divide the average number of moles of O by the smaller of the average numbers of moles of Mg or of O.

7. Write the empirical formula for the oxide of magnesium.

Pre-Laboratory Assignment

1. Why is it hazardous for you to look directly at the Mg in the crucible when it is heated and first reacts with atmospheric oxygen?

2. (a) Why should you always use crucible tongs when you handle the crucible and its cover?

(b) Why will you have to begin the Procedure again if the crucible cover falls and breaks at any time after you complete Step 6?

(c) Why will you add a few drops of water to the white reaction product in the crucible (Step 14)?

(d) Why will the crucible and its contents gain mass as a result of heating the Mg in air?

3. A student determined the empirical formula of potassium oxide using the procedure of this experiment. She obtained the following data:

mass of crucible and cover, g	28.288
mass of crucible, cover, and K, g	28.709
mass of crucible, cover, and potassium oxide, g	28.793

Use these data to determine the empirical formula of potassium oxide. The molar mass of potassium (K) is 39.10 g/mol.

ISBN 0-87540-606-8

modular · laboratory · program · in · chemistry

publisher: H. A. Neidig   editor: M. L. Gillette

Observing Single Replacement Reactions

prepared by **M. L. Gillette**, Indiana University Kokomo;
H. A. Neidig, Lebanon Valley College; and **J. N. Spencer**, Franklin and Marshall College

Purpose of the Experiment

Determine the relative activities of aluminum, iron, copper and hydrogen.

Background Required

You should be familiar with basic laboratory techniques for measuring mass and volume. You should be familiar with the concepts associated with oxidation and solution chemistry and the symbolism associated with chemical equations.

Background Information

A **single replacement reaction** occurs when atoms of one metal transfer one or more electrons to cations of another metal or to hydrogen ions (H^+). We represent a single replacement reaction by the general reaction shown in Equation 1, where A, a metal, reacts with BC, an ionic compound of a different metal (B) and the charge-balancing anion (C). The products are B, now a free metal, and AC, a metal salt.

$$A(s) + BC(aq) \rightarrow B(s) + AC(aq) \tag{Eq. 1}$$

The process involves the transfer of electrons from A to B, and we say that A **replaces** B in BC.

In this type of reaction, there is competition for electrons between the two elements, A and B. One element loses an electron (or electrons) to the element that is less able to lose electrons.

Reaction of a Metal with a Strong Acid

Some metals can displace hydrogen ions (H^+) from a solution of a strong acid. If we place zinc (Zn) in hydrochloric acid (HCl), a strong acid, the Zn begins to dissolve forming a colorless solution of zinc chloride ($ZnCl_2$), and bubbles of colorless hydrogen gas (H_2) form in the solution. Equation 2 represents this reaction.

$$Zn(s, \text{bluish–white}) + 2\,HCl(aq, \text{colorless}) \rightarrow ZnCl_2(aq, \text{colorless}) + H_2(g, \text{colorless}) \tag{Eq. 2}$$

In this reaction, Zn loses electrons and H^+ ions gain electrons, forming H_2. The reverse reaction, shown in Equation 3, does not occur. (N.R. means "no reaction".)

$$ZnCl_2(aq) + H_2(g) \rightarrow \text{N.R.} \tag{Eq. 3}$$

Because Zn loses electrons to H^+, but H_2 does not lose electrons to Zn^{2+}, we say that Zn is more **active** than H_2. Any metal that is less active than H_2 will not react when added to HCl solution. Metals more active than H_2 react with 6M HCl with differing vigor; some metals cause a rapid release of H_2 gas, others a very slow release.

Reaction of a Metal with the Salt of a Different Metal

A second type of single replacement reaction involves a metal and a solution of the salt of a different metal. For example, if we place copper (Cu) in a silver nitrate ($AgNO_3$) solution, copper(II) nitrate, $Cu(NO_3)_2$, and silver (Ag) form, as shown in Equation 4.

$$Cu(s, reddish) + 2\ AgNO_3(aq, colorless) \rightarrow Cu(NO_3)_2(aq, blue) + 2\ Ag(s, white) \quad (Eq.\ 4)$$

Cu loses electrons to Ag^+. The reverse reaction, shown in Equation 5, does not occur.

$$2\ Ag(s, white) + Cu(NO_3)_2(aq, blue) \rightarrow N.R. \quad (Eq.\ 5)$$

We say that Cu is a more active metal than Ag because Cu loses electrons more easily than Ag does.

Solutions of metal salts may be acidic. Therefore, sometimes H_2 bubbles are seen when we add a metal to a solution of a different metal salt. H_2 production may or may not be accompanied by the reaction of the metal with the other metal salt. In order to conclude whether or not one of the metals is more active than the other, we must look for other evidence of a reaction having taken place.

Example

Problem

You are asked to determine whether Zn is more active than Cu, and to write equations for the reactions you observe.

When you place Cu in a colorless zinc sulfate ($ZnSO_4$) solution, there is no apparent change in the solution. When you place Zn in a blue copper(II) sulfate ($CuSO_4$) solution, a reddish solid forms in solution, and the intensity of blue in the solution markedly decreases.

Solution

(1) Write the equation for the reaction of Cu with $ZnSO_4$.

$$Cu(s, reddish) + ZnSO_4(aq, colorless) \rightarrow N.R.$$

(2) Write the equation for the reaction of Zn with $CuSO_4$.

$$Zn(s, bluish-white) + CuSO_4(aq, blue) \rightarrow ZnSO_4(aq, colorless) + Cu(s, reddish)$$

(3) Draw conclusions from your observations regarding the relative reactivity of Cu and Zn.

Zn is more active than Cu, because Zn can transfer electrons to Cu^{2+}, but Cu cannot transfer electrons to Zn^{2+}.

In This Experiment

You will establish the relative activities of aluminum (Al), iron (Fe), copper (Cu), and hydrogen (H_2). You will determine the order from observations of chemical changes that occur when you combine various pairs of these elements and solutions of their salts and of the metals with 6M HCl.

Procedure

Note: • *Dispose of your reaction mixtures and rinses as directed by your laboratory instructor.*
 • *Record all of your data on your Data and Observations sheet.*

I. Reacting Metals with 6*M* HCl

1. Obtain three 4-cm pieces each of Al wire, Cu wire, and Fe wire. Clean each piece of metal with sandpaper to remove any metallic oxide and expose the metal surface. Record the physical characteristics of the metals such as their color, texture, and luster.

2. Use a Pasteur or Beral pipet to transfer 3 mL of 6*M* HCl into each of three test tubes.

Caution: *6M HCl is a corrosive, toxic substance that can cause burns.*

Record your description of 6*M* HCl, including its color.

Note: *For each of the following steps, observe the reaction mixture for 5 min before recording any observations. In some parts of this experiment, a reaction will not occur. When such is the case, write N.R. in the appropriate space on your Data and Observations sheet.*

3. Place a 4-cm piece of Al wire in one test tube containing 6*M* HCl. Place a 4-cm piece of Cu wire in the second test tube. Place a 4-cm piece of Fe wire in the third test tube.
 After 5 min, record your observations of each reaction mixture.

4. Discard the acid solutions and any unreacted metal in the containers specified by your laboratory instructor. Wash the test tubes. Rinse them with tap water and then with distilled or deionized water.

II. Reacting Metals with Solutions of Metallic Salts

5. Use a Pasteur or Beral pipet to transfer 3 mL of 0.5*M* aluminum sulfate, $Al_2(SO_4)_3$, into each of two test tubes.
 Record your description of 0.5*M* $Al_2(SO_4)_3$, including its color.

6. Place a 4-cm piece of Fe wire in one of the test tubes containing 0.5*M* $Al_2(SO_4)_3$. Place a 4-cm piece of Cu wire in the second test tube.
 After 5 min, record your observations of each reaction mixture.

7. Discard the solutions and any unreacted metal into the containers specified by your laboratory instructor. Wash the test tubes. Rinse them with tap water and then with distilled water.

8. Use a Pasteur or Beral pipet to transfer 3 mL of 0.5*M* iron(II) sulfate ($FeSO_4$) into each of two test tubes.

Record your description of 0.5*M* $FeSO_4$, including its color.

9. Place a 4-cm piece of Al wire in one of the test tubes containing 0.5*M* $FeSO_4$. Place a 4-cm piece of Cu wire in the second test tube.

After 5 min, record your observations of each reaction mixture.

10. Discard the solutions and any unreacted metal into the containers specified by your laboratory instructor. Wash the test tubes. Rinse them with tap water and then with distilled water.

11. Use a Pasteur or Beral pipet to transfer 3 mL of 0.5*M* $CuSO_4$ into each of two test tubes.

Record your description of 0.5*M* $CuSO_4$, including its color.

12. Place a 4-cm piece of Al wire in one of the test tubes containing 0.5*M* $CuSO_4$. Place a 4-cm piece of Fe wire in the second test tube.

After 5 min, record your observations of each reaction mixture.

13. Discard the solutions and any unreacted metal into the containers specified by your laboratory instructor. Wash the test tubes. Rinse them with tap water and then with distilled water.

Post-Laboratory Questions

Use the spaces provided for the answers and additional paper if necessary.

1. Assume that you mixed HCl and $CuSO_4$ solutions. If a reaction would have occurred, write an equation for the reaction. If no reaction occurs, explain why.

2. Zn is less active than Mg. Write the equations describing what occurs when you mix:

    (a) Zn with $0.5M$ magnesium chloride, $MgCl_2$. (If no reaction occurs, write N.R.)

    (b) Mg with $0.5M$ $ZnCl_2$. (If no reaction occurs, write N.R.)

3. Based upon your laboratory results, which metal, Cu, Fe, or Al, would be most affected by acid rain? Briefly explain.

4. Based on your laboratory results, will acidic foods cooked in a cast iron skillet become Fe^{2+}-enriched because of a reaction between the acidic food and the skillet? Briefly explain.

Data and Observations

I. Reacting Metals with 6*M* HCl

metal/reactant	appearance
Al	
Fe	
Cu	
6*M* HCl	

metal	description of reaction mixture 5 min after mixing with 6M HCl	did reaction occur? (Y or N.R.)
Al		
Fe		
Cu		

II. Reacting Metals with Solutions of Metallic Salts

appearance of 0.5*M* $Al_2(SO_4)_3$:

metal	description of reaction mixture 5 min after mixing with 0.5M $Al_2(SO_4)_3$	did reaction occur? (Y or N.R.)
Fe		
Cu		

appearance of 0.5*M* FeSO$_4$:

metal	description of reaction mixture 5 min after mixing with 0.5M FeSO$_4$	did reaction occur? (Y or N.R.)
Al		
Cu		

appearance of 0.5*M* CuSO$_4$:

metal	description of reaction mixture 5 min after mixing with 0.5M CuSO$_4$	did reaction occur? (Y or N.R.)
Al		
Fe		

Calculations and Conclusions

I. Reacting Metals with 6M HCl

1. Write the equation for each reaction you observed when you placed the metal wires in 6M HCl.

2. On the basis of your results in Part I, arrange the three metals and H_2 in order of their decreasing relative activity. Use the symbols ">", and "=" when appropriate. Briefly explain the basis of the order you selected.

_____   _____   _____   _____

II. Reacting Metals with Solutions of Metallic Salts

3. Write chemical equations for the reactions you observed when you put each metal wire in 0.5M $Al_2(SO_4)_3$.

4. Write chemical equations for the reactions you observed when you put each metal wire in 0.5M $FeSO_4$.

5. Write chemical equations for the reactions you observed when you put each metal wire in 0.5M CuSO$_4$.

6. Based on your results in Parts I and II, arrange the three metals and H$_2$ in order of decreasing relative activity.

_____ > _____ > _____ > _____

7. Summarize the chemical evidence you obtained to justify your activity series.

name partner section date

Pre-Laboratory Assignment

1. What hazards should you know about when you work with:

   (a) 6*M* HCl?

   (b) 0.5*M* $CuSO_4$?

2. Explain why the reaction shown below is a single replacement reaction.

$$Zn(s, \text{bluish–white}) + CuSO_4(aq, \text{blue}) \rightarrow ZnSO_4(aq, \text{colorless}) + Cu(s, \text{reddish})$$

3. How will you recognize that a single replacement reaction has occurred when you combine:

   (a) an active metal with 6*M* HCl?

   (b) an active metal with $CuSO_4$ solution?

4. You are given pieces of Zn and Al, and amounts of $ZnSO_4$ and $Al_2(SO_4)_3$ solutions.

   (a) What combinations of these four substances would you make to illustrate that Zn is less active than Al?

(b) What specific observations would you make after you've prepared each combination?

(c) Write equations describing your observations.

ISBN 0-87540-610-6

REAC
611

modular · laboratory · program · in · chemistry
publisher: H. A. Neidig   editor: M. L. Gillette

Observing Some Double Replacement Reactions

prepared by **M. L. Gillette**, Indiana University Kokomo;
H. A. Neidig, Lebanon Valley College; and **J. N. Spencer**, Franklin and Marshall College

Purpose of the Experiment

Observe whether a reaction occurs when two aqueous solutions of ionic compounds are mixed. Write chemical equations for observed reactions.

Background Required

You should be familiar with basic laboratory techniques for mixing solutions and observing reactions, and with the symbolism associated with chemical equations.

Background Information

A general representation of one type of reaction that may occur when solutions of two ionic compounds are mixed is shown in Equation 1.

$$AB + CD \rightarrow AD + CB \qquad \text{(Eq. 1)}$$

We interpret this general reaction to mean that A in the ionic compound AB replaces C in the ionic compound CD to form a new compound, AD. At the same time, B in the reactant AB replaces D in the reactant CD to form a new compound, CB. Because two replacements occur, we call this type of reaction a **double replacement reaction** or a **double displacement reaction**.

For example, if we mix solutions of silver nitrate ($AgNO_3$) and sodium chloride (NaCl), a white solid appears. This solid, or **precipitate**, forms because at least one of the reaction products is insoluble in the solution. The formation of the precipitate indicates that a reaction has occurred. We can determine which reaction product is the white precipitate by consulting solubility data in a chemistry handbook, or a table such as Table 1. We can then write an equation (Equation 2) to represent the reaction.

$$AgNO_3(aq, \text{colorless}) + NaCl(aq, \text{colorless}) \rightarrow AgCl(s, \text{white}) + NaNO_3(aq, \text{colorless}) \qquad \text{(Eq. 2)}$$

Table 1 *Properties of some compounds*

compound formula	color and physical state at room temperature	solubility in water	compound formula	color and physical state at room temperature	solubility in water
AgCl	white solid	insoluble	KOH	white solid	soluble
AgNO$_3$	white solid	soluble	Mg(OH)$_2$	white solid	insoluble
BaCl$_2$	white solid	soluble	Mg(NO$_3$)$_2$	white solid	soluble
BaCO$_3$	white solid	insoluble	MgSO$_4$	white solid	soluble
Ba(NO$_3$)$_2$	white solid	soluble	NaCl	white solid	soluble
BaSO$_4$	white solid	insoluble	Na$_2$CO$_3$	white solid	soluble
CaCl$_2$	white solid	soluble	NaI	white solid	soluble
CaCO$_3$	white solid	insoluble	NaNO$_3$	white solid	soluble
CaSO$_4$	white solid	insoluble	Na$_2$SO$_4$	white solid	soluble
CuCl$_2$	blue/green solid	soluble	PbCl$_2$	white solid	insoluble
Cu(NO$_3$)$_2$	blue solid	soluble	PbCO$_3$	white solid	insoluble
Cu(OH)$_2$	blue solid	insoluble	PbI$_2$	yellow solid	insoluble
CuSO$_4$	blue solid	soluble	Pb(NO$_3$)$_2$	white solid	soluble
HCl	colorless gas	soluble	Pb(OH)$_2$	white solid	insoluble
KCl	white solid	soluble	ZnCl$_2$	white solid	soluble
K$_2$CO$_3$	white solid	soluble	Zn(NO$_3$)$_2$	white solid	soluble
KNO$_3$	white solid	soluble	Zn(OH)$_2$	white solid	insoluble

If the double displacement involves an acid and a base, the only evidence of a reaction will be an increase in temperature. In some cases, one of the products could be an unstable substance that dissociates into a gas and water.

In order to conclude that a double displacement reaction has taken place, we must observe some change in the reaction mixture. Observations may include precipitate formation, temperature change, gas evolution, and/or a color change.

In some cases, such as when we mix NaCl and potassium nitrate (KNO$_3$) solutions, no reaction occurs. In such instances, we write an expression in the form shown in Equation 3, where "N.R." means "no reaction".

$$NaCl(aq, colorless) + KNO_3(aq, colorless) \rightarrow N.R. \qquad (Eq.\ 3)$$

Example

Problem Mix magnesium nitrate, Mg(NO$_3$)$_2$, and potassium hydroxide (KOH) solutions. Identify the white precipitate that forms and write an equation for this double displacement reaction.

Solution *(1) Identify the two possible reaction products, assuming a double displacement reaction occurred.*

The products would be Mg(OH)$_2$ and KNO$_3$.

(2) Check Table 1 to find the solubility of Mg(OH)$_2$ and of KOH.

According to Table 1, Mg(OH)$_2$ is insoluble in water, and KOH is soluble in water. Therefore, the white precipitate must be Mg(OH)$_2$.

(3) Write the equation for the double displacement reaction.

$$Mg(NO_3)_2(aq, colorless) + 2 KOH(aq, colorless) \rightarrow Mg(OH)_2(s, white) + 2 KNO_3(aq, colorless)$$

In This Experiment

You will mix a series of solutions in pairs. You will observe each reaction mixture, and decide whether or not a reaction occurred on the basis of a color change or the formation of a precipitate. For those combinations that do react, you will write equations representing the reactions.

Procedure

Caution: *Wear departmentally approved safety goggles while doing this experiment. Always use caution in the laboratory. Many chemicals are potentially harmful. Prevent contact with your eyes, skin, and clothing. Avoid ingesting any of the reagents.*

Note: • *In this experiment, you will work with one or more of the following laboratory assignments:*
   (1) 0.1M barium chloride ($BaCl_2$) and 0.1M sodium sulfate (Na_2SO_4)
   (2) 0.1M NaCl and 0.3M KOH
   (3) 0.1M sodium iodide (NaI) and 0.1M lead(II) nitrate, $Pb(NO_3)_2$
   (4) 0.3M sodium carbonate (Na_2CO_3) and 0.1M calcium chloride ($CaCl_2$)
   (5) 0.3M $Mg(NO_3)_2$ and 0.3M KOH
   (6) 0.1M copper(II) nitrate, $Cu(NO_3)_2$, and 0.3M KOH
   • *Dispose of your reaction mixtures and rinses according to your laboratory instructor's directions.*
   • *Record all of your data on your Data and Observations sheet.*

Caution: *0.1M Lead nitrate is oxidant and irritating. 0.1M Copper (II) nitrate ($Cu(NO_3)_2$) is corrosive and oxidant.*

1.   Use a Pasteur or Beral pipet to transfer 3 mL of the first of the solutions in your first designated pair into a test tube. Record your description of this reactant.
   Record your description of the second reactant.
   Using a Pasteur or Beral pipet, add 3 mL of the second solution in the pair to the first solution in the test tube.
   Thoroughly stir the mixture for 15 s with a clean, glass stirring rod.

2.   Carefully observe the reaction mixture. Record your description of the mixture, noting any precipitate formation or color change.

3.   Discard the contents of your test tube into a 150-mL beaker labeled "Rinse Water and Reaction Mixtures." Thoroughly rinse the test tube and stirring rod with tap water, then with distilled or deionized water. Pour the rinses into the discard beaker.
   Transfer the contents of the beaker into the container specified by your laboratory instructor. Rinse the 150-mL beaker with tap water and transfer these rinses to the laboratory instructor's appropriately labeled discard container.

4. Proceed to the next assigned pair of solutions. Repeat Steps 1–3. Discard each reaction mixture into the appropriately labeled container specified by your laboratory instructor.

5. Repeat Step 4 until you have completed all the experiments assigned to you by your laboratory instructor. You may be asked to share laboratory observations with other students so that everyone has a complete set of data.

Caution: *Wash your hands thoroughly with soap or detergent before leaving the laboratory.*

Post-Laboratory Questions

Use the spaces provided for the answers and additional paper if necessary.

1. Instead of following the procedure for laboratory assignment 3 exactly, a student placed the $Pb(NO_3)_2$ solution in the test tube and then added NaI solution. What, if any, effect would the procedural change make on the student's results for this test? Briefly explain.

2. A student tried to detect the presence of calcium ion (Ca^{2+}) in milk by adding Na_2SO_4 solution to a sample of milk. Briefly comment on the likely results of her experiment.

3. On the basis of the reactions of the solutions you used in this experiment and information in Table 1, what conclusion can you draw about the general water solubility of:

(a) compounds in which Na^+ is the cation?

(b) compounds in which NO_3^- is the anion?

(c) compounds in which Pb^{2+} is the cation?

Data and Observations

laboratory assignment	formula of reactant 1	description of reactant 1	formula of reactant 2	description of reactant 2

description of mixture after mixing:

laboratory assignment	formula of reactant 1	description of reactant 1	formula of reactant 2	description of reactant 2

description of mixture after mixing:

laboratory assignment	formula of reactant 1	description of reactant 1	formula of reactant 2	description of reactant 2

description of mixture after mixing:

laboratory assignment	*formula of reactant 1*	*description of reactant 1*	*formula of reactant 2*	*description of reactant 2*
_____	_____	_____	_____	_____

description of mixture after mixing:

laboratory assignment	*formula of reactant 1*	*description of reactant 1*	*formula of reactant 2*	*description of reactant 2*
_____	_____	_____	_____	_____

description of mixture after mixing:

laboratory assignment	*formula of reactant 1*	*description of reactant 1*	*formula of reactant 2*	*description of reactant 2*
_____	_____	_____	_____	_____

description of mixture after mixing:

Calculations and Conclusions

Complete the following table for each laboratory assignment that you performed or for which you have data. If a reaction occurred, write an equation for the reaction.

laboratory assignment _____   reactant _____   reactant _____

Did reaction occur? (Y/N) _____   If yes, write chemical equation:

laboratory assignment _____   reactant _____   reactant _____

Did reaction occur? (Y/N) _____   If yes, write chemical equation:

laboratory assignment _____   reactant _____   reactant _____

Did reaction occur? (Y/N) _____   If yes, write chemical equation:

laboratory assignment _____   reactant _____   reactant _____

Did reaction occur? (Y/N) _____   If yes, write chemical equation:

---

laboratory assignment _____   reactant _____   reactant _____

Did reaction occur? (Y/N) _____   If yes, write chemical equation:

---

laboratory assignment _____   reactant _____   reactant _____

Did reaction occur? (Y/N) _____   If yes, write chemical equation:

Pre-Laboratory Assignment

1. What hazards should you be aware of when you work with the copper or lead compounds used in this experiment?

2. List two evidences you will look for that will indicate whether a double displacement reaction occurred.

3. Use the information in Table 1 to describe what you would observe if you mixed the following pairs of solutions. Assume a double replacement reaction occurred in each case. Include the color of all solutions and/or precipitates.

    (a) $BaCl_2$ and $Pb(NO_3)_2$

    (b) $Pb(NO_3)_2$ and Na_2CO_3

4. Write equations for the double displacement reactions you expect to occur when the following pairs of solutions are mixed.

    (a) $BaCl_2$ and $Pb(NO_3)_2$

    (b) $Pb(NO_3)_2$ and Na_2CO_3

ISBN 0-87540-611-4

modular · laboratory · program · in · chemistry

publisher: H. A. Neidig
editor: M. L. Gillette

Classifying Some Chemical Reactions

prepared by **M. L. Gillette**, Indiana University Kokomo, and
H. A. Neidig, Lebanon Valley College

Purpose of the Experiment

Perform a series of chemical reactions. Write chemical equations for the reactions, based on your observations. Classify each reaction as one of four general types.

Background Required

You should be familiar with basic laboratory techniques for volume measurement. You should be able to recognize when a substance is in its elemental form, and when it is a compound.

Background Information

Many chemical reactions can conveniently be classified as one of four general types. The classification is based on the nature of the chemical transformation involved.

Four Types of Chemical Reactions

Type I: Combination, Synthesis, or Formation Reactions

A **combination**, **synthesis**, or **formation reaction** occurs when two substances, usually in their elemental forms, combine to form a compound. Equation 1 shows a generalized combination reaction, while Equation 2 shows a specific example.

$$A + B \rightarrow AB \qquad \text{(Eq. 1)}$$

$$2\ Ca(s) + O_2(g) \rightarrow 2\ CaO(s) \qquad \text{(Eq. 2)}$$

Type II: Decomposition Reactions

A **decomposition reaction** occurs when a compound breaks apart into two or more products. Equation 3 shows a generalized example, while Equation 4 shows a specific example.

$$AB \rightarrow A + B \qquad \text{(Eq. 3)}$$

$$2\ HgO(s) \rightarrow 2\ Hg(\ell) + O_2(g) \qquad \text{(Eq. 4)}$$

Type III: Single Displacement or Single Replacement Reactions

When the uncombined form of one element displaces (and replaces) another element in a compound, forming a new compound, we call the process a **single displacement** or **single replacement reaction**. Equation 5 shows a generalized example, and Equation 6 shows a specific example.

$$A + BC \rightarrow AC + B \tag{Eq. 5}$$

$$2\,Al(s) + 6\,HNO_3(aq) \rightarrow 2\,Al(NO_3)_3(aq) + 3\,H_2(g) \tag{Eq. 6}$$

Type IV: Double Displacement or Double Replacement Reactions

A **double displacement** or **double replacement reaction** occurs when ions from two different ionic compounds change places to form two new compounds. One of the compounds formed usually has one of the following forms: a solid, called a **precipitate;** a slightly dissociated compound, such as water; or a gas. Equation 7 shows a generalized example, and Equation 8 shows a specific example. In Equation 8, $PbCl_2(s)$ is the precipitate.

$$AB + CD \rightarrow AD + CB \tag{Eq. 7}$$

$$Pb(NO_3)_2(aq) + 2\,NaCl(aq) \rightarrow PbCl_2(s) + 2\,NaNO_3(aq) \tag{Eq. 8}$$

Many reactions are **exothermic,** meaning that they release heat to their surroundings. Other reactions are **endothermic,** meaning that these reactions absorb heat from their surroundings. Therefore, temperature changes in a chemical system can be evidence that a chemical reaction has occurred.

Example

Problem

When shiny red–brown (elemental) copper mesh is heated in an open crucible, the mesh turns black. If prodded with a stirring rod, the black mesh crumbles. What general type of reaction has occurred?

Solution

(1) Analyze your observations.

Because only one reaction product was observed, for the purposes of this experiment, we will conclude that there was probably no second reaction product. The only substance with which the copper came into contact was the air, a mixture of compounds the most reactive of which is oxygen (O_2). Thus, we can conclude that the reaction must have occurred because, on heating, the metallic copper (Cu) reacted with atmospheric O_2.

(2) Suggest a formula for the reaction product.

We can conclude that Cu combined with O_2 to form black CuO.

(3) Write the chemical equation for the reaction.

$$2\,Cu(s,\ brown) + O_2(g) \rightarrow 2\,CuO(s,\ black)$$

(4) Classify the reaction as one of the four general types.

This reaction is a combination reaction (Type I) because two reactants (Cu and O_2) combined to form one product (CuO).

In This Experiment

You will perform several chemical reactions. Based on your observations, you will write chemical equations for the reactions. You will also classify each reaction as one of the four general types. The chemical formulas for the elements and compounds you will be working with are listed in Table 1.

Table 1 *Chemical formulas for some of the elements and compounds encountered in this experiment*

chemical name	chemical formula
ammonia	NH_3
ammonium carbonate	$(NH_4)_2CO_3$
carbon(IV) oxide (carbon dioxide)	CO_2
copper	Cu
copper(II) sulfate (cupric sulfate)	$CuSO_4$
copper(II) sulfate pentahydrate	$CuSO_4 \cdot 5H_2O$
hydrochloric acid	HCl
iron	Fe
iron(II) sulfate (ferrous sulfate)	$FeSO_4$
magnesium	Mg
sodium hydroxide	$NaOH$

Procedure

Caution: *Wear departmentally approved safety goggles while doing this experiment. Always use caution in the laboratory. Many chemicals are potentially harmful. Prevent contact with your eyes, skin, and clothing. Avoid ingesting any of the reagents. Take care not to burn your skin when using the Bunsen burner.*

Note:
- *Perform all or some of the following experiments, as directed by your laboratory instructor.*
- *Follow your laboratory instructor's directions for: dispensing and transferring solutions to a test tube using a Pasteur or Beral pipet; estimating the volume of solution transferred; and stirring reaction mixtures in a test tube.*
- *Dispose of your reaction mixtures, rinses, and used litmus paper according to your laboratory instructor's directions.*
- *Record all of your data on your Data and Observations sheet.*

I. Reacting Mg with 0.1 *M* HCl

Caution: *Magnesium ribbon is flammable and moisture-sensitive. 0.1M HCl is toxic and corrosive. The gas produced by the reaction of Mg and HCl solution also is flammable. Be sure that there are no Bunsen burner flames in the area where you are performing this reaction.*

1. Transfer a 0.5-cm piece of Mg ribbon to the bottom of a clean 15 × 100-mm test tube. Record your description of the Mg ribbon.
Record your description of 0.1 *M* HCl.

2. Holding the bottom of the test tube containing the Mg ribbon, transfer 2 mL of 0.1 *M* HCl into the test tube. Observe the reaction mixture for evidence of a chemical reaction. Note any temperature change in the outside wall of the test tube. Record all observations.

3. Transfer the contents of your test tube to a small beaker. Rinse the test tube with tap water, then with distilled or deionized water. Transfer all rinses into the beaker. Transfer the beaker contents into the collection container specified by your laboratory instructor.

II. Reacting 0.1 M $CuSO_4$ with 0.1 M NaOH

Caution: *$CuSO_4$ is toxic. NaOH is toxic and corrosive.*

4. Record your descriptions of 0.1 M $CuSO_4$ and 0.1 M NaOH.

5. Transfer 10 drops of 0.1 M $CuSO_4$ into a clean, dry test tube. Add 2 drops of 0.1 M NaOH to the test tube. Thoroughly mix the solutions. Record your description of the reaction mixture and any evidence of temperature change in the mixture.

6. Dispose of your reaction mixture as you did in Step 3. Rinse and dry the test tube.

III. Reacting $CuSO_4 \cdot 5H_2O$ with Heat and Water

A. Heating $CuSO_4 \cdot 5H_2O$

7. Transfer the amount of $CuSO_4 \cdot 5H_2O$ that fills the end of a clean, dry microspatula into a clean, dry test tube. Record your description of $CuSO_4 \cdot 5H_2O$.

8. Grasp the top of the test tube with a test tube holder. Holding the test tube as shown in Figure 1, strongly heat the bottom of the test tube in a Bunsen burner flame until you see a change in the appearance of the solid. Remove the test tube from the flame. Carefully observe both the solid and the inner test tube wall near the open end of the test tube. Allow the tube to cool. Record your descriptions of the test tube inner wall and of the solid remaining in the test tube.

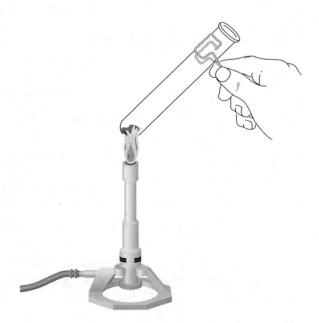

Figure 1 *Heating $CuSO_4 \cdot 5H_2O$ in a test tube*

B. Adding Water to Product of Heated CuSO₄ · 5H₂O

9. Add 1 drop of distilled water to the solid remaining in the test tube. Record your description of the solid after the addition of water.

10. Dispose of your reaction mixture as you did in Step 3. Rinse and dry the test tube and microspatula.

IV. Reacting 0.1 M CuSO₄ with Steel Wool (Fe)

11. Record your descriptions of steel wool (Fe) and 0.1 M CuSO₄.

12. Obtain an amount of steel wool equivalent to the volume of a pencil eraser. Use a glass stirring rod to carefully slide the steel wool to the bottom of a clean, dry test tube. Add 2 mL of 0.1 M CuSO₄ solution to the test tube. Stir the mixture for 2−3 min.
　　Observe the appearance of the steel wool and solution. Record your descriptions of the steel wool and reaction mixture after the reaction has occurred.

13. Dispose of the reaction mixture in the collection container specified by your laboratory instructor. Use your stirring rod to carefully transfer the steel wool from the test tube to the specified collection container. Rinse and dry the stirring rod and test tube.

V. Heating (NH₄)₂CO₃

14. Record your description of (NH₄)₂CO₃. Transfer the amount of (NH₄)₂CO₃ that fills the end of a clean microspatula to the bottom of a clean, dry test tube.

> **Note:** *Red litmus paper turns blue in the presence of bases, such as NH₃.*

15. Place a piece of red litmus paper on a small watch glass. Moisten the litmus paper with 1−2 drops of distilled water. The moist paper will cling to the watch glass. Record your description of the moistened litmus paper.

> **Caution:** *The vapors created by heating (NH₄)₂CO₃ are toxic and irritating.*

16. Working in a ***fume hood,*** strongly heat the bottom of the test tube containing the (NH₄)₂CO₃ in a Bunsen burner flame, holding it as shown in Figure 1. Carefully observe both the solid and the inner test tube wall near the open end of the test tube.

17. Holding the open end of the test tube about 6 in. from your face, ***carefully*** fan the fumes from the test tube toward your nose, as shown in Figure 2 on the next page. Note the odor of the vapors. Do ***not*** hold the test tube directly under your nose.
　　Then, invert the watch glass, and position it so that the moist litmus paper covers the open end of the test tube. Observe the color of the litmus paper. Record your descriptions of: what happened to the solid (NH₄)₂CO₃; the inner wall of the test tube; the odor of the vapors; and the color of the litmus paper after exposure to the vapors.

Figure 2 *Detecting odors*

18. Dispose of your reaction mixture as you did in Step 3. Discard the litmus paper in the specified container. Rinse and dry the watch glass, microspatula, test tube, and any other glassware you used in this experiment.

Caution: *Wash your hands thoroughly with soap or detergent before leaving the laboratory.*

Post-Laboratory Questions

Use the spaces provided for the answers and additional paper if necessary.

1. (a) Write chemical equations for the decomposition reactions you observed.

(b) What evidence do you have indicating the presence of the reaction products you listed? Briefly explain.

(c) Write chemical equations for the single displacement reactions you observed.

(d) Besides being single displacement reactions, what, if anything, did the reactions you listed in (c) have in common?

2. First-generation automobile air bags contain a mixture of sodium azide (NaN_3), potassium nitrate (KNO_3), and silicon dioxide (SiO_2).

(a) The chemical reaction responsible for inflating this type of air bag is shown in Equation 9.

$$2 \, NaN_3(s) \rightarrow 2 \, Na(s) + 3 \, N_2(g) \qquad \text{(Eq. 9)}$$

Classify this reaction as one of the four general types.

(b) The sodium (Na) formed when the air bag fills with nitrogen (N_2) reacts with KNO_3, as shown in Equation 10.

$$10 \, Na(s) + 2 \, KNO_3(s) \rightarrow K_2O(s) + 5 \, Na_2O(s) + N_2(g) \qquad \text{(Eq. 10)}$$

Classify this reaction as one of the four general types. (Note: K_2O is a simple byproduct of the primary reaction, so you can ignore this product when you consider your answer.)

3. Iron is a relatively inexpensive and strong building material, but it tends to react with atmospheric O_2 to form iron(III) oxide, Fe_2O_3. In the presence of atmospheric moisture, Fe_2O_3 forms hydrated iron(III) oxide ($Fe_2O_3 \cdot nH_2O$), commonly called rust.

(a) Write the chemical equation for the oxidation of Fe to form Fe_2O_3.

(b) Classify the reaction you described in 3(a) as one of the four general types.

(c) Write the chemical equation for the hydration of Fe_2O_3 to form rust.

(d) Classify the reaction you described in 3(c) as one of the four general types.

name   partner   section   date

Data and Observations

I. Reacting Mg with 0.1M HCl

	appearance of reactants	appearance of products	other observations (if any)
Mg			
0.1M HCl			

II. Reacting 0.1M CuSO$_4$ with 0.1M NaOH

	appearance of reactants	appearance of products	other observations (if any)
0.1M CuSO$_4$			
0.1M NaOH			

III. Reacting CuSO$_4 \cdot$ 5H$_2$O with Heat and Water

A. Heating CuSO$_4 \cdot$ 5H$_2$O

	appearance of reactant	appearance of products	other observations (if any)
CuSO$_4 \cdot$ 5H$_2$O			

B. Adding Water to Product of Heated CuSO$_4 \cdot$ 5H$_2$O

	appearance of reactants	appearance of products	other observations (if any)
product of heated CuSO$_4 \cdot$ 5H$_2$O			
water			

IV. Reacting 0.1 *M* CuSO$_4$ with Steel Wool (Fe)

	appearance of reactants	*appearance of products*	*other observations (if any)*
0.1*M* CuSO$_4$			
Fe			

V. Heating (NH$_4$)$_2$CO$_3$

	appearance of reactants	*appearance of products*	*other observations (if any)*
(NH$_4$)$_2$CO$_3$			
moistened red litmus paper			

Calculations and Conclusions

Write your conclusions in the spaces provided.

I. Reacting Mg with 0.1 M HCl

evidence of a chemical reaction:

chemical equation for the reaction:

general reaction type:

II. Reacting 0.1 M CuSO$_4$ with 0.1 M NaOH

evidence of a chemical reaction:

chemical equation for the reaction:

general reaction type:

III. Reacting CuSO$_4 \cdot$ 5H$_2$O with Heat and Water

A. Heating CuSO$_4 \cdot$ 5H$_2$O

evidence of a chemical reaction:

chemical equation for the reaction:

general reaction type:

B. Adding Water to Product of Heated $CuSO_4 \cdot 5H_2O$

evidence of a chemical reaction:

chemical equation for the reaction:

general reaction type:

IV. Reacting 0.1M $CuSO_4$ with Steel Wool (Fe)

evidence of a chemical reaction:

chemical equation for the reaction:

general reaction type:

V. Heating $(NH_4)_2CO_3$

evidence of a chemical reaction:

chemical equation for the reaction:

general reaction type:

Pre-Laboratory Assignment

1. What hazards should you be aware of when working with:

    (a) heated $(NH_4)_2CO_3$?

    (b) $0.1M$ HCl?

    (c) $0.1M$ NaOH?

2. Distinguish between:

    (a) exothermic and endothermic reactions

    (b) single and double displacement reactions

3. Identify the general reaction types illustrated by the following equations:

   (a) $N_2(g) + 3 H_2(g) \rightarrow 2 NH_3(g)$

   (b) $NaOH(aq) + HCl(aq) \rightarrow NaCl(aq) + H_2O(\ell)$

   (c) $Cu(s) + 2 AgNO_3(aq) \rightarrow Cu(NO_3)_2(aq) + 2 Ag(s)$

4. What would you observe if you performed the reaction shown in:

   (a) Equation 6?

   (b) Equation 8?

ISBN 0-87540-613-0

m o d u l a r · l a b o r a t o r y · p r o g r a m · i n · c h e m i s t r y

publisher: H. A. Neidig   editor: M. L. Gillette

Writing, Interpreting, and Balancing Chemical Equations

prepared by **M. L. Gillette**, Indiana University Kokomo, and
H. A. Neidig, Lebanon Valley College

Purpose of the Exercise

Practice writing, interpreting, and balancing chemical equations.

Background Information

Chemical reactions occur when the atoms of elements or compounds, called **reactants,** interact to form new atomic combinations, called **products**. We can represent this process in the most general terms as shown in Equation 1, in which the arrow signifies "yield" or "produce".

$$\text{reactants} \rightarrow \text{products} \tag{Eq. 1}$$

For each reaction, we can write an expression called a **chemical equation,** in which we represent the specific reactants and products using their chemical formulas.

Writing and Interpreting Chemical Equations

If we heat lead sulfide (PbS), a metallic blue solid, with iron (Fe), a metallic gray solid, we produce elemental lead (Pb), a silvery blue solid, and iron(II) sulfide (FeS), a brownish black solid. We can describe this reaction using the chemical equation shown in Equation 2.

$$\text{PbS(s, metallic blue)} + \text{Fe(s, metallic gray)} \xrightarrow{\text{heat}} \text{Pb(s, silvery blue)} + \text{FeS(s, brownish black)} \tag{Eq. 2}$$

In Equation 2, the information in parentheses following the chemical formulas indicates the physical state ("s" for solid, "ℓ" for liquid, or "g" for gas) and color of each substance. If the substance is dissolved in water, we represent its physical state using "aq", which stands for **aqueous**. Sometimes we omit the color descriptions in order to simplify the notation. The information above the reaction arrow describes specific reaction conditions, such as the application of heat or the presence of an acid.

CENGAGE Learning™

The Significance of a Chemical Formula

In order to write chemical equations, we must be able to recognize the number of atoms of each element that are present in one unit of a substance. For example, the formula for sodium sulfide is Na_2S. The subscript 2 following Na indicates that there are two sodium (Na) atoms in one Na_2S unit. If no subscript is shown, it means the subscript is 1. Hence, one Na_2S unit also contains one sulfur (S) atom. Similarly, in one potassium dichromate ($K_2Cr_2O_7$) unit, there are two potassium (K) atoms, two chromium (Cr) atoms, and seven oxygen (O) atoms.

In the chemical formulas for some compounds, groups of atoms are enclosed in parentheses, with a subscript following the second parenthesis. Consider strontium iodate, $Sr(IO_3)_2$. The subscript 3 following the O indicates that one iodate ion (IO_3^-) contains three oxygen atoms. The subscript 2 following the second parenthesis indicates that one unit of strontium iodate contains two IO_3^- ions. Therefore, one $Sr(IO_3)_2$ unit is made up of one strontium (Sr) atom, two iodine (I) atoms, and six oxygen atoms.

When we write a chemical equation, we use chemical formulas to represent the relevant elements and compounds *in the forms in which they participate in the reaction.* For example, when metal atoms are in their **elemental**, or chemically uncombined (with other elements), form, they react as if they were individual atoms. Therefore, we can represent them in a chemical equation simply by using the appropriate chemical symbol, as shown in Equation 2 for Fe and Pb.

In contrast, some nonmetallic elements exist in nature as **molecules** composed of two or more atoms of the element, held together by shared electron pairs. For example, elemental hydrogen, nitrogen, oxygen, and halogens (fluorine, chlorine, bromine, and iodine) occur naturally as **diatomic** (two-atom) molecules: H_2, N_2, O_2, F_2, Cl_2, Br_2, and I_2, respectively. Thus, we refer to O_2 as elemental oxygen (or simply oxygen) and to O as an oxygen atom. Similarly, phosphorus (P) occurs naturally as P_4, and sulfur occurs as S_8. Therefore, these are the formulas that we use to represent these elements in chemical equations. For example, carbon (C) reacts with oxygen (O_2) to form carbon(IV) dioxide (CO_2), as shown in Equation 3.

$$C(s) + O_2(g) \rightarrow CO_2(g) \qquad \text{(Eq. 3)}$$

Balancing Chemical Equations

Chemical equations illustrate a principle called **conservation of matter:** matter can neither be created nor destroyed. Therefore, every reactant atom must end up in one of the reaction products, and the reaction products cannot contain any atoms that were not part of the reactants. We can establish the correct reactant–product proportions for a reaction by **balancing** the chemical equation for the reaction. Sometimes, an equation is already balanced when it is written in its simplest form. For example, Equation 2 is balanced, because there is one Pb atom, one S atom, and one Fe atom on each side.

Usually, we have to add numbers to a chemical equation so that the equation shows the correct proportions of reactants and products. Consider the reaction of magnesium (Mg) with CO_2 to produce magnesium oxide (MgO). Equation 4 shows this reaction, but the equation is unbalanced.

$$Mg(s, \text{metallic gray}) + CO_2(g, \text{colorless}) \rightarrow MgO(s, \text{white}) + C(s, \text{black}) \quad \text{(Eq. 4)}$$

As written, the reactant side has one Mg atom, one C atom, and two O atoms, while the product side has one Mg atom, one O atom, and one C atom.

To indicate that more than one unit of a particular species is involved in a chemical reaction, we use a number, called a **coefficient**, written to the left of the symbol or formula for the species. If no coefficient is shown, it means that the coefficient is 1. To balance Equation 4, we can write a coefficient of 2 in front of Mg and MgO, as shown in Equation 4a.

$$2 \ Mg(s, \text{metallic gray}) + CO_2(g, \text{colorless}) \rightarrow 2 \ MgO(s, \text{white}) + C(s, \text{black}) \quad \text{(Eq. 4a)}$$

Now there are two Mg atoms, two O atoms, and one C atom on each side, so the equation is balanced.

We could use other sets of coefficients to balance Equation 4. For example, coefficients of 4, 2, 4, and 2, respectively, would also work, as shown in Equation 4b.

$$4 \ Mg(s, \text{metallic gray}) + 2 \ CO_2(g, \text{colorless}) \rightarrow 4 \ MgO(s, \text{white}) + 2 \ C(s, \text{black}) \quad \text{(Eq. 4b)}$$

However, to simplify chemical equations as much as possible, we use the smallest whole number coefficients possible. Because 4 and 2 are divisible by 2 to yield whole numbers, we prefer to write the equation as shown in Equation 4a.

We must be careful not to alter the chemical formula for any reactant or product species while balancing an equation. If we change the subscripts in the chemical formula for a species, we alter the identity of that substance. The resulting equation may be balanced, but it will represent a different reaction from the one represented by the original, unbalanced equation.

Example

Problem Write and balance the chemical equation for the reaction of gaseous elemental oxygen with solid elemental phosphorus to form solid tetraphosphorus decaoxide (P_4O_{10}).

Solution *(1) Write the formulas for the reactants, then the reaction arrow, and then the formula for the product, including notation to indicate the physical state of each.*

$$P_4(s) + O_2(g) \rightarrow P_4O_{10}(s)$$

(2) Determine whether or not the equation is balanced as written.
The equation is not balanced, because although there are four P atoms on each side, there are only two O atoms on the reactant side, while there are ten O atoms on the product side.
(3) Determine the correct coefficients for each reactant and product, in order to balance the equation.

$$P_4(s) + 5 \ O_2(g) \rightarrow P_4O_{10}(s)$$

With the addition of a coefficient of 5 for O_2, the equation is now balanced. There are four phosphorus atoms and ten oxygen atoms on each side.

In This Exercise

You will gain experience writing, interpreting, and balancing chemical equations by completing Problem Sets 1–4.

name | partner | section | date

Problem Set 1

Write a chemical equation describing each of the following reactions, including the physical states and colors of the reactants and products. Also indicate reaction conditions, where applicable.

1. White crystalline sodium chloride ($NaCl$) reacts with sulfuric acid (H_2SO_4), a colorless liquid, to form hydrogen chloride (HCl), a colorless gas, and sodium hydrogen sulfate ($NaHSO_4$), a white solid.

2. When we heat solid red mercury(II) sulfide (HgS) in oxygen, the products are silvery gaseous mercury (Hg) and sulfur dioxide (SO_2), a colorless gas.

3. When we mix colorless liquid cyclohexene (C_6H_{10}) with bromine, a dark red liquid, 1,2-dibromocyclohexane ($C_6H_{10}Br_2$), a colorless liquid, is produced.

Problem Set 2

Indicate the number of atoms of each element present in one unit of the following compounds.

1. BaO Ba ______ O ______

2. Li_2O Li ______ O ______

3. $AlCl_3$ Al ______ Cl ______

4. Cr_2O_3 Cr ______ O ______

5. $Al(NO_3)_3$ Al ______ N ______ O ______

6. $Ca_3(PO_4)_2$ Ca ______ P ______ O ______

7. $HC_2H_3O_2$ H ______ C ______ O ______

8. $(NH_4)_2Cr_2O_7$ N ______ H ______ Cr ______ O ______

Problem Set 3

Correctly balance each of the following equations, using the appropriate coefficients. Do not change any of the subscripts.

1. $CH_4(g) + O_2(g) \rightarrow CO_2(g) + H_2O(\ell)$

2. $Pb(NO_3)_2(aq) + HCl(aq) \rightarrow PbCl_2(s) + HNO_3(aq)$

3. $N_2(g) + H_2(g) \rightarrow NH_3(g)$

4. $N_2(g) + O_2(g) \rightarrow N_2O_4(g)$

5. $C_4H_8(OH)_2(aq) + H_2O_2(aq) \rightarrow C_4H_6O_2(aq) + H_2O(\ell)$

Problem Set 4

1. Correctly balance each of the following equations, using the appropriate coefficients. Do not change any of the subscripts.

   (a) $Ca(s) + H_2(g) \rightarrow CaH_2(s)$

   (b) $SO_3(g) + H_2O(\ell) \rightarrow H_2SO_4(aq)$

   (c) $H_2(g) + F_2(g) \rightarrow HF(g)$

(d) $H_2O_2(aq) \rightarrow H_2O(\ell) + O_2(g)$

(e) $NH_4NO_2(s) \xrightarrow{\text{heat}} N_2(g) + H_2O(g)$

(f) $BeCl_2(s) + LiH(s) \rightarrow BeH_2(s) + LiCl(s)$

(g) $Fe(s) + O_2(g) \rightarrow Fe_2O_3(s)$

(h) $CH_4(g) + H_2O(g) \xrightarrow[\text{pressure}]{\text{heat, catalyst,}} CO(g) + H_2(g)$

(i) $AsH_3(g) \rightarrow As(s) + H_2(g)$

(j) $NaHCO_3(s) \xrightarrow{\text{heat}} Na_2CO_3(s) + CO_2(g) + H_2O(g)$

(k) $NO_2(g) + H_2O(\ell) \rightarrow HNO_3(aq) + NO(g)$

(l) $Fe(s) + H_2O(g) \xrightarrow{\text{heat}} Fe_3O_4(s) + H_2(g)$

(m) $Na_2O_2(s) + H_2O(\ell) \rightarrow NaOH(s) + O_2(g)$

(n) $HNO_3(aq) \xrightarrow{\text{light}} NO_2(g) + H_2O(\ell) + O_2(g)$

(o) $NH_3(g) + O_2(g) \rightarrow NO(g) + H_2O(g)$

2. What is the sum of the coefficients in:

   (a) Equation 4a?

   (b) Equation 3?

3. Correctly balance each of the following equations.

   (a) $Cu(s) + HNO_3(aq) \rightarrow Cu(NO_3)_2(aq) + NO(g) + H_2O(\ell)$

   (b) $Bi_2S_3(s) + O_2(g) \rightarrow Bi_2O_3(s) + SO_2(g)$

   (c) $CaSiO_3(s) + HF(aq) \rightarrow SiF_4(g) + CaF_2(s) + H_2O(\ell)$

   (d) $(NH_4)_2Cr_2O_7(s) \xrightarrow{\text{heat}} N_2(g) + H_2O(g) + Cr_2O_3(s)$

ISBN 0-87540-614-9

A N A L
620

modular · laboratory · program · in · chemistry

publisher: H. A. Neidig

editor: M. L. Gillette

Separating and Identifying FD&C Dyes Using Paper Chromatography

prepared by **Peter Markow**, Saint Joseph College, CT, and
M. L. Gillette, Indiana University Kokomo

Purpose of the Experiment

Determine the retention factors (R_f) of seven FD&C dyes on chromatography paper, using 0.1% sodium chloride as the mobile phase. Use paper chromatography to separate and identify which of these seven dyes are in unknown mixtures and selected commercial products.

Background Required

You should be familiar with the concepts associated with intermolecular interactions and chemical equilibrium.

Background Information

Chromatography consists of a group of techniques used to separate mixtures into their component parts. All chromatography techniques involve a **stationary phase** (usually liquid or solid) and a **mobile phase** (liquid or gas). The mixture being separated is usually placed on the stationary phase. The mobile phase then moves along the stationary phase, carrying some or all of the mixture with it, resulting in the separation of the mixture into its components.

In **paper chromatography**, we apply, or "spot", a sample of the mixture we wish to separate near the bottom of a piece of chromatography paper, which serves as the stationary phase. The location of the spotted area is called the **origin**. Then we place the bottom edge of the paper in a solvent, which acts as the mobile phase. The mobile phase is drawn up the paper by capillary action, because the solvent molecules are attracted to water molecules bound to the cellulose fibers in the paper.

The leading edge of the mobile phase is called the **solvent front.** When the solvent front reaches the origin, each component of the sample is preferentially attracted to either the stationary or mobile phase by intermolecular interactions. Frequently, sample components are somewhat attracted to both phases. Each component establishes equilibrium between the two phases, as shown by Equation 1.

$$\text{component-mobile phase} \rightleftharpoons \text{component-stationary phase} \qquad \text{(Eq. 1)}$$

As the solvent front continues to move up the paper, fresh solvent reaches the remaining sample component molecules, establishing new equilibria. At the same time, sample components that are dissolved in the mobile phase encounter fresh stationary phase, and new equilibria are established. Thus, due to differences in their molecular structures, the components of a mixture move up the paper at different rates, causing them to separate and produce a characteristic pattern called a **chromatogram.** We characterize the movement of each component on the developed chromatogram by its **retention** or **retardation factor** (**R_f**), defined by Equation 2.

$$R_f = \frac{\text{distance traveled by component, cm}}{\text{distance traveled by solvent front, cm}} \qquad \text{(Eq. 2)}$$

The R_fs of specific mixture components are reproducible, as long as the phase compositions remain constant. If the mobile phase contains a volatile substance, such as ethyl alcohol, its percent composition may change during the analysis, due to evaporation. To prevent evaporation from occurring, we cover the developing chamber.

We can identify unknown mixture components by comparing their R_fs with those of known compounds chromatographed under the same experimental conditions. Frequently, we can use additional data from chromatograms, such as color, to confirm identifications based on R_f comparisons.

Example

Problem   Separate and identify the components of an unknown (unk) dye mixture containing two of the following certified food, drug, and cosmetic (FD&C) dyes: red 3 (r3), red 40 (r40), yellow 5 (y5), and yellow 6 (y6).

Solution   *(1) Chromatograph the unknown mixture, along with samples of each of the possible components. After developing the chromatogram, mark the final position of the solvent front (see Figure 1).*

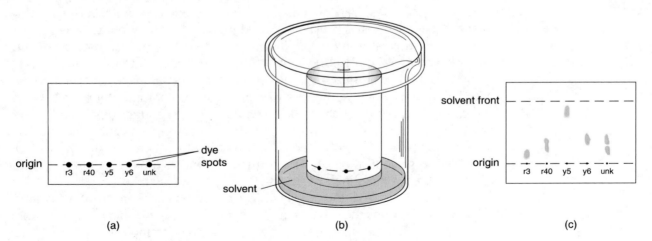

Figure 1 *Preparing a chromatogram: (a) spotting the samples; (b) developing the chromatogram; (c) marking the final position of the solvent front and the components*

*(2) Measure the distance between the origin line and the solvent front. Outline each component, and note its color. Measure the distance between the origin line and the **center** of each component. Calculate the R_f for each component, using Equation 2.*
   See Table 1.

Table 1 *Data from the chromatography of r3, r40, y5, y6, and an unknown mixture of two of these dyes*

dye	distance from origin line, cm	R_f	color
solvent front	5.0		
r3	0.4	0.4 cm/5.0 cm = 0.08	red
r40	1.3	1.3 cm/5.0 cm = 0.26	red
y5	3.9	3.9 cm/5.0 cm = 0.78	yellow
y6	2.1	2.1 cm/5.0 cm = 0.42	orange
unk- #1	2.0	2.0 cm/5.0 cm = 0.40	orange
unk- #2	1.2	1.2 cm/5.0 cm = 0.24	red

(3) Identify the components of the unknown mixture, using your calculated R_fs and the observed component colors.

Based on the R_fs and the colors, the unknown contains red 40 and yellow 6.

In This Experiment

You will chromatograph seven FD&C dyes, both individually and in various combinations, in order to establish their R_fs. Then you will identify which of these dyes are present in several unknown mixtures and in various commercial products, such as food products and felt-tip pens.

Procedure

> **Caution:** *Wear departmentally approved safety goggles while doing this experiment. Always use caution in the laboratory. Many chemicals are potentially harmful. Prevent contact with your eyes, skin, and clothing. Avoid ingesting any of the reagents.*

> **Note:** • *Obtain your unknown samples using the method indicated by your laboratory instructor.*
> • *Record all observations and data on your Data and Observations sheet.*
> • *Dispose of your reaction mixtures according to your laboratory instructor's directions.*

I. Characterizing FD&C Dyes and Identifying FD&C Dyes in Unknown Mixtures

1. Prepare a chromatography chamber by measuring 7 mL of 0.1% sodium chloride (NaCl) into a 250-mL beaker. Cover the beaker with a Petri dish cover. Repeat the process with a second beaker and cover.

> **Note:** *Handle chromatography paper only by its edges.*

2. Obtain two 7.5 × 13.5-cm pieces of chromatography paper. Using a **pencil**, draw a line along the long axis of each paper, 1 cm from the bottom edge (see Figure 2). Beginning 1.5 cm from the left edge of the first piece of paper, make eleven vertical pencil marks on the line at 1-cm intervals. Label the top left corner of this paper "1". Make ten vertical marks on the line of the second piece of paper. Label the top left corner of this paper "2".

On paper 1, label your marks on the origin line as shown in Figure 2(a). Label your marks on paper 2 as shown in Figure 2(b).

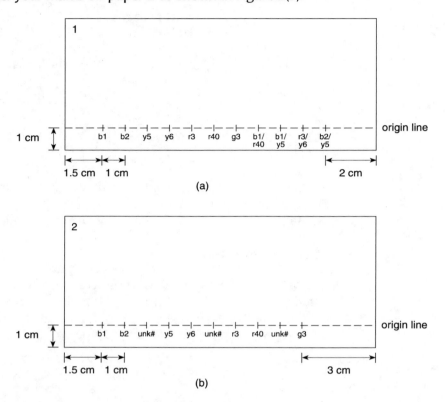

Figure 2 *(a) Labeling chromatography paper 1 (b) Labeling chromatography paper 2*

Caution: *Dyes will stain clothing and skin.*

---

3. Use a separate medicine dropper or Pasteur pipet for each dye. Transfer one drop of each of the seven pure dye solutions into separate wells of a 24-well plate. Record the well designation for each dye.

Use separate droppers or pipets. Transfer one drop of each of the three different unknown mixtures assigned to you into separate wells in your well plate. Record the identification code and well designation for each unknown mixture.

Note: *Always allow a spotted area to dry completely before adding more dye to it.*

4. Using a clean wooden toothpick for each dye and unknown, spot each sample at the appropriately labeled mark on your chromatography paper. To do so, first place the smaller end of the toothpick in the dye solution. Then, keeping the toothpick vertical, touch the end of the toothpick to the designated position on the origin line.

For the four combinations of two dyes, spot the second dye directly on top of the first. Allow each application to dry before respotting.

Spot each of the unknown mixtures four or five times at the appropriately labeled position. Allow each application to dry before respotting.

5. Carefully roll each piece of chromatography paper along its short axis to form a cylinder. Place the spotted areas on the outside and the origin line at the bottom, as shown in Figure 3. Staple the ends of each paper together **with the edges touching, but not overlapping.**

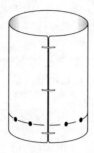

Figure 3 *Preparing spotted chromatography paper for development*

6. Remove the cover from one of your beakers. Place one of your paper cylinders in the beaker, as shown in Figure 1(b). Make sure that the spotted areas are above the solvent surface and that the cylinder does not touch the beaker wall. Replace the cover.

Repeat this process with your second cylinder and second beaker.

> **Note:** *You may perform Steps 8–11 while your chromatograms from Part I are developing. If you do so, you must check the chambers frequently to monitor the progress of the solvent fronts. When the solvent fronts are about 1.5 cm from the top of the papers, begin Step 7.*

7. Remove each cylinder from its beaker when the solvent front is about 1.5 cm from the top of the paper. Carefully remove the staples from the cylinder.

While the paper is drying, the solvent will continue to move up the paper for a few more minutes. Draw a pencil line marking the position of the solvent front after the solvent has stopped moving, but before the chromatogram is completely dry. Allow the paper to air dry. Be sure to retain the chromatograms for use in the Calculations and Conclusions section.

Cover the beakers with the Petri dishes, and set aside for use in Part II.

II. Identifying FD&C Dyes in Commercial Products

8. Obtain seven commercial product solutions and three felt-tip pens from your laboratory instructor. Record the product names and identification codes of the solutions and pens.

9. Prepare a third piece of 7.5 × 13.5-cm chromatography paper, following the directions for paper 2 in Step 2. Label the origin line marks with the identification codes of the commercial product solutions and pens you have selected. Label the paper "3" in the top left corner.

> **Note:** *The dyes in some commercial products are much less concentrated than the pure dye solutions used in Part I. Therefore, you may need to spot each commercial product solution several times, until the color intensity of the spotted sample is close to that of the applications made in Part I. Allow each application to dry before respotting.*
>
> *In contrast, the dyes in felt-tip pens are highly concentrated, so you should spot each one only once. To keep the pen spot small, do not allow the pen tip to contact the paper for longer than 1 s. Note that the dyes used in some felt-tip pens cannot be separated and identified using the procedures described in this experiment.*

10. Repeat Steps 3 and 4, spotting the commercial product solutions and pens instead of the FD&C dyes, dye mixtures, and unknown solutions on chromatography paper 3.

11. Repeat Steps 5–7.

Dispose of your solutions and toothpicks. Rinse your glassware and well plate with tap water, then distilled water. Drain the glassware and well plate to dry.

12. Using a pencil, outline each component on the three dry chromatograms. Be sure to retain the chromatograms for use in the Calculations and Conclusions section.

Caution: *Wash your hands thoroughly with soap or detergent before leaving the laboratory.*

Post-Laboratory Questions

Use the spaces provided for the answers and additional paper if necessary.

1. In Part I, was the calculated R_f of each FD&C dye when chromatographed alone identical to the R_f of that dye when chromatographed as part of a mixture? Briefly explain.

2. Why was it important that:

(a) you marked the origin line and component locations on the paper with a pencil, and not a pen or marker?

(b) when you put the dry paper cylinders into the beakers, the spotted areas were above the solvent surface?

3. Why were all your calculated R_fs less than 1.0? Is it possible for an R_f to be greater than 1.0? Briefly explain.

4. How would your results have been affected if you had used water-insoluble pens, instead of water-soluble ones, in Part II of this experiment? Briefly explain.

Data and Observations

I. Characterizing FD&C Dyes and Identifying FD&C Dyes in Unknown Mixtures

well designations for known dyes

       red 3 (r3)   _____   blue 1 (b1)   _____

       red 40 (r40)   _____   blue 2 (b2)   _____

       yellow 5 (y5)   _____   green 3 (g3)   _____

       yellow 6 (y6)   _____

identification codes of assigned unknowns: _____   _____   _____

well designations for unknowns: _____   _____   _____

II. Identifying FD&C Dyes in Commercial Products

product name	identification code	product name	identification code

Calculations and Conclusions

Show your calculations in the space provided.

I. Characterizing FD&C Dyes and Identifying FD&C Dyes in Unknown Mixtures

Do the following calculations using your chromatograms 1 and 2. Record the results in Table 2 later in this experiment.

1. Measure the distance the solvent front moved, in centimeters.

2. Find the center of each outlined component. Measure the distance from the origin line to the center of each component, in centimeters. Record this measurement as the distance the component moved.

3. Calculate the R_f for each pure FD&C dye, using Equation 2.

4. Find the average R_f for each pure dye, using the R_fs you determined from chromatograms 1 and 2.

5. Calculate the R_f for each component of the known mixtures and each component of your three unknowns.

6. Identify the component dyes in your three unknown mixtures. To do so, use the colors and the average R_fs of the pure dyes, along with any changes you observed in R_fs when these dyes were part of the known mixtures.

Table 2 *Data and Calculations for Part I*

	chromatogram 1				chromatogram 2		

distance solvent front moved, cm _____   distance solvent front moved, cm _____

dye identification	distance component moved, cm	R_f	dye identification	distance component moved, cm	R_f	average R_f
blue 1			blue 1			
blue 2			blue 2			
yellow 5			yellow 5			
yellow 6			yellow 6			
red 3			red 3			
red 40			red 40			
green 3			green 3			

mixture identification		distance component moved, cm	R_f	mixture identification		distance component moved, cm	R_f
blue 1/ red 40:	blue 1			blue 1/ yellow 5:	blue 1		
	red 40				yellow 5		
red 3/ yellow 6:	red 3			blue 2/ yellow 5:	blue 2		
	yellow 6				yellow 5		

spot identification		distance component moved, cm	color	R_f
unk #_____ :	component 1			
	component 2			
	component 3			
	component 4			
unk #_____ :	component 1			
	component 2			
	component 3			
	component 4			
unk #_____ :	component 1			
	component 2			
	component 3			
	component 4			

unknown # _____ contains _____

_____

_____

_____

unknown # _____ contains _____

_____

_____

_____

unknown # _____ contains _____

_____

_____

_____

II. Identifying FD&C Dyes in Commercial Products

7. Repeat Calculations 1, 2, 5, and 6 for chromatogram 3. Record your results in Table 3 on the next page.

8. Using the solution/pen spot colors and the average R_fs for the seven FD&C dyes from Part I, identify the component dyes in each product. Record your results in Table 3 on the next page.

Table 3 *Data and Calculations for Part II*

distance solvent front moved, cm _____

product name	pen/solution identification code	distance component moved, cm	color	R_f	dye identification

name | partner | section | date

Pre-Laboratory Assignment

1. Why is it important to not spill FD&C dyes on your skin or clothing?

2. Define the following terms as they relate to this experiment.

(a) origin

(b) solvent front

(c) R_f

3. (a) What will you use as the stationary phase in this experiment?

(b) What will you use as the mobile phase in this experiment?

4. Why is it important for you to:

(a) keep the beaker containing the mobile phase covered while preparing your chromatography paper and developing your chromatograms?

(b) remove the chromatography paper from the beaker before the solvent front reaches the top of the paper?

5. In the Example in the Background Information, what experimental evidence confirmed that the unknown mixture contained two FD&C dyes? Briefly explain.

6. After developing a chromatogram, a student determined that a dye component traveled 3.5 cm and the solvent front traveled 6.2 cm. Calculate the R_f of the dye.

ISBN 0-87540-620-3

modular · laboratory · program · in · chemistry

publisher: H. A. Neidig

editor: M. L. Gillette

Identifying Cations in a Solution

prepared by **H. A. Neidig**, Lebanon Valley College; **J. N. Spencer**, Franklin and Marshall College; and **M. L. Gillette**, Indiana University Kokomo

Purpose of the Experiment

Develop a procedure using chemical reactions to detect the presence of barium, lead(II), and iron(III) ions in solution. Use the procedure to identify these cations in an unknown solution containing one or more of them. Write chemical equations for the observed reactions.

Background Required

You should know how to write and balance chemical equations.

Background Information

Chemists are frequently asked to identify the components of a sample. The process of doing so is called **qualitative analysis.**

Many ionic compounds dissolve in water, producing positive and negative ions in solution. The positive ions are called **cations,** and the negative ions are called **anions.** To perform a qualitative analysis to establish the presence of specific ions in a solution, we test small portions of the solution with selected reagents. We choose reagents that produce known reactions with the possible solution components. These reactions include formation of insoluble substances, formation of soluble complex ions, and solution color changes. Sometimes we can also use visible characteristics of the sample, such as its color, to establish the presence of a particular ion.

For example, we can use an aqueous solution of potassium iodide (KI) to establish the presence of lead(II) ion (Pb^{2+}) in a solution. When solutions of lead nitrate, $Pb(NO_3)_2$, a source of Pb^{2+}, and KI are mixed, a yellow solid precipitates from the solution. We can describe this reaction using a **molecular equation,** which shows all of the species in their undissociated forms. Equation 1 on the next page shows the molecular equation for this reaction.

$$Pb(NO_3)_2(aq, \text{colorless}) + 2\ KI(aq, \text{colorless}) \rightarrow PbI_2(s, \text{yellow}) + 2\ KNO_3(aq, \text{colorless}) \quad (\text{Eq. 1})$$

In contrast, the **complete ionic equation** for a reaction shows all of the ions of the dissociated substances, as well as the undissociated substances. Equation 2 shows the complete ionic equation for the reaction of $Pb(NO_3)_2$ and KI.

$$Pb^{2+}(aq) + 2\ NO_3^-(aq) + 2\ K^+(aq) + 2\ I^-(aq) \rightarrow PbI_2(s, \text{yellow}) + 2\ K^+(aq) + 2\ NO_3^-(aq) \quad (\text{Eq. 2})$$

Ions that appear on both sides of the reaction arrow in a complete ionic equation are called **spectator ions.** These ions are not directly involved in the reaction. When we eliminate them from the complete ionic equation, we are left with the **net ionic equation** for the reaction. Equation 3 shows the net ionic equation for the reaction of $Pb(NO_3)_2$ and KI.

$$Pb^{2+}(aq) + 2\ I^-(aq) \rightarrow PbI_2(s, \text{yellow}) \quad (\text{Eq. 3})$$

This characteristic reaction serves as the basis for a qualitative test for Pb^{2+}.

Example

Problem   Design a procedure using KI and dimethylglyoxime (DMG) solutions to determine whether an unknown solution contains nickel(II) ion (Ni^{2+}), Pb^{2+}, or both.

Solution   *(1) Determine whether or not Ni^{2+} and Pb^{2+} solutions react individually with KI solution. To do so, add KI solution to a Ni^{2+} solution, then to a Pb^{2+} solution.*

No signs of reaction are evident when Ni^{2+} solution is mixed with KI solution. In contrast, a yellow precipitate forms when Pb^{2+} solution is mixed with KI solution, indicating that a reaction has occurred.

(2) Determine whether or not Ni^{2+} and Pb^{2+} solutions react individually with DMG solution. To do so, add DMG solution to a Ni^{2+} solution, then to a Pb^{2+} solution.

No signs of reaction are evident when Pb^{2+} solution is added to DMG solution. In contrast, a bright red color develops when Ni^{2+} solution is mixed with DMG solution, indicating that a reaction has occurred.

(3) Add KI solution to a sample of the unknown solution.

A yellow precipitate forms, which establishes the presence of Pb^{2+}.

(4) Add DMG solution to another sample of the unknown solution.

No change occurs in the solution. We conclude that the unknown solution contains only Pb^{2+}.

In This Experiment

You will work with aqueous solutions of iron(III) nitrate, $Fe(NO_3)_3$, barium nitrate ($Ba(NO_3)_2$), and $Pb(NO_3)_2$. You will observe the chemical behavior of iron(III) ions (Fe^{3+}), barium ions (Ba^{2+}), and Pb^{2+} when mixed individually with various solutions. Then, you will identify these cations in an unknown solution that may contain one, two, or all three of them.

Some of the compounds and complex ions that you will observe are described in Table 1.

Table 1 *Some compounds and complex ions containing Fe^{3+}, Pb^{2+}, or Ba^{2+}*

ion or compound	reagent	reaction product
Fe^{3+}	potassium thiocyanate (KSCN) solution	$[FeSCN]^{2+}$(aq, red)
Ba^{2+}	sodium sulfate (Na_2SO_4) solution	$BaSO_4$(s, white)
Pb^{2+}	hydrochloric acid (HCl) solution	$PbCl_2$(s, white)
Pb^{2+}	Na_2SO_4 solution	$PbSO_4$(s, white)
$PbSO_4$	sodium acetate ($NaC_2H_3O_2$) solution	$[Pb(C_2H_3O_2)_4]^{2-}$(aq, colorless)

Procedure

Caution: *Wear departmentally approved safety goggles while doing this experiment. Always use caution in the laboratory. Many chemicals are potentially harmful. Prevent contact with eyes, skin, and clothing. Avoid ingesting any of the reagents.*

Note:
- *Follow your laboratory instructor's directions for: dispensing and transferring solutions to a test tube, using a Pasteur or Beral pipet; estimating the volume of solution thus transferred; and mixing reaction mixtures in a test tube.*
- *If you use a glass stirring rod to mix solutions, be certain to rinse it well with tap water, then with distilled water, after each use.*
- *Dispose of your reaction mixtures and rinses according to your laboratory instructor's directions.*
- *Record all of your observations on your Data and Observations sheet.*

I. Labeling Your Equipment

1. Label three 16×150-mm test tubes "1", "2", and "3". Place these test tubes in a test tube rack.

Label a 150-mL beaker, "Discarded Fe^{3+} Mixtures", a second 150-mL beaker, "Discarded Ba^{2+} Mixtures", and a third 150-mL beaker, "Discarded Pb^{2+} Mixtures".

Label a 250-mL beaker, "Discarded Rinses".

II. Studying Some Reactions of Fe^{3+}

Caution: *$Fe(NO_3)_3$ solution is an oxidant and an irritant. KSCN solution is toxic and an irritant.*

2. Obtain 6 mL of $0.1M$ $Fe(NO_3)_3$ in a clean 10-mL graduated cylinder. Transfer 2 mL of this solution into each of your numbered test tubes.

3. Add 3 drops of $0.1M$ KSCN to the solution in test tube 1. Thoroughly mix. Record your observations.

Caution: *HCl is toxic and corrosive. Na_2SO_4 is an irritant.*

4. Add 15 drops of $1M$ HCl to the solution in test tube 2, and thoroughly mix. Record your observations.

5. Add 3 drops of $0.1M$ Na_2SO_4 to the solution in test tube 3, and thoroughly mix. Record your observations.

6. Add 5 mL of $3M$ $NaC_2H_3O_2$ to the reaction mixture in test tube 3, and thoroughly mix. Record your observations.

7. Discard the contents of test tubes 1, 2, and 3 into the "Discarded Fe^{3+} Mixtures" beaker.

Rinse the three test tubes and your graduated cylinder with tap water, then distilled or deionized water. Pour the rinses into your "Discarded Rinses" beaker.

III. Studying Some Reactions of Ba^{2+}

> **Caution:** $Ba(NO_3)_2$ is toxic and an oxidant.

8. Obtain 6 mL of $0.1M$ $Ba(NO_3)_2$ in your rinsed 10-mL graduated cylinder. Transfer 2 mL of $0.1M$ $Ba(NO_3)_2$ into each of your numbered test tubes.

9. Follow the procedure described in Steps 3–6.

10. Discard the contents of your test tubes into the "Discarded Ba^{2+} Mixtures" beaker.

Rinse the test tubes and graduated cylinder, following the instructions in Step 7.

IV. Studying Some Reactions of Pb^{2+}

> **Caution:** $Pb(NO_3)_2$ is an oxidant and an irritant.

11. Obtain 6 mL of $0.1M$ $Pb(NO_3)_2$ in your rinsed 10-mL graduated cylinder. Transfer 2 mL of $0.1M$ $Pb(NO_3)_2$ into each of your numbered test tubes.

12. Follow the procedure described in Steps 3–6.

13. Discard the contents of your test tubes into the "Discarded Pb^{2+} Mixtures" beaker.

Rinse the test tubes, following the instructions in Step 7. Then transfer the contents of each discarded mixtures beaker into the appropriately labeled collection container. Rinse the discard beakers and graduated cylinder following the instructions in Step 7, and allow to drain.

V. Analyzing the Unknown Solution

14. Obtain from your laboratory instructor 6 mL of an unknown solution in your graduated cylinder. This solution may contain one, two, or all three of the cations you are studying in this experiment. Record the identification code of your unknown solution.

15. Transfer 2 mL of your unknown solution into each of your numbered test tubes.

16. Follow the procedure described in Steps 3–6.

17. Discard the contents of your test tubes into the appropriate discard container provided by your laboratory instructor.
Rinse your test tubes following the instructions in Step 7.

18. Transfer the contents of the Discarded Rinses beaker into the appropriately labeled container provided by your laboratory instructor. Rinse the beaker and graduated cylinder with tap water, then distilled water, and allow to drain.

Caution: *Wash your hands thoroughly with soap or detergent before leaving the laboratory.*

Post-Laboratory Questions

Use the spaces provided for the answers and additional paper if necessary.

1. Complete the following flowchart illustrating a procedure you could use to separate and identify Ba^{2+}, Pb^{2+}, and Fe^{3+} ions in a mixture, based on the data you collected in this experiment.

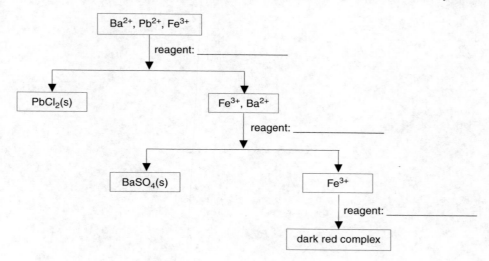

2. A student came late to the laboratory, and she was rushing to complete this experiment. In her haste, she mixed the HCl and Na_2SO_4 solutions together in a test tube before adding them to a sample of her unknown (Part V). Describe the problem she might have had in identifying the cations in her unknown.

3. A student was given an unknown solution and told that it contained either chloride ion (Cl^-) or sulfate ion (SO_4^{2-}), or both. The student was also told that $PbCl_2$ is insoluble in $3M$ $NaC_2H_3O_2$. Using the test solutions from this experiment, devise a procedure the student could use to determine which anion(s) is/are present in the unknown.

Data and Observations

II. Studying Some Reactions of Fe^{3+}

solution	test solution added	observations
$Fe(NO_3)_3$	KSCN	
$Fe(NO_3)_3$	HCl	
$Fe(NO_3)_3$	Na_2SO_4	
$Fe(NO_3)_3/Na_2SO_4$	$NaC_2H_3O_2$	

III. Studying Some Reactions of Ba^{2+}

solution	test solution added	observations
Ba(NO$_3$)$_2$	KSCN	
Ba(NO$_3$)$_2$	HCl	
Ba(NO$_3$)$_2$	Na$_2$SO$_4$	
Ba(NO$_3$)$_2$/Na$_2$SO$_4$	NaC$_2$H$_3$O$_2$	

IV. Studying Some Reactions of Pb^{2+}

solution	test solution added	observations
Pb(NO$_3$)$_2$	KSCN	
Pb(NO$_3$)$_2$	HCl	
Pb(NO$_3$)$_2$	Na$_2$SO$_4$	
Pb(NO$_3$)$_2$/Na$_2$SO$_4$	NaC$_2$H$_3$O$_2$	

V. Analyzing the Unknown Solution

identification code of unknown _____

solution	test solution added	observations
unknown	KSCN	
unknown	HCl	
unknown	Na_2SO_4	
unknown/Na_2SO_4	$NaC_2H_3O_2$	

Calculations and Conclusions

II. Studying Some Reactions of Fe^{3+}

1. Write the molecular, complete ionic, and net ionic equations for each reaction you observed.

III. Studying Some Reactions of Ba^{2+}

2. Write the molecular, complete ionic, and net ionic equations for each reaction you observed.

IV. Studying Some Reactions of Pb^{2+}

3. Write the molecular, complete ionic, and net ionic equations for each reaction you observed.

V. Analyzing the Unknown Solution

4. Identify which of the three cations you studied in this experiment is/are present in your unknown. Indicate the specific experimental evidence you used to make the identification(s).

unknown identification code _____

cation(s) present _____

name | partner | section | date

Pre-Laboratory Assignment

1. Describe the hazards you should be aware of when working with:

(a) $Pb(NO_3)_2$

(b) 1*M* HCl

2. Define the following terms as they apply to this experiment.

(a) qualitative analysis

(b) spectator ion

3. When we mix aqueous solutions of silver nitrate ($AgNO_3$) and sodium chloride (NaCl), a white precipitate of silver chloride (AgCl) forms in the reaction mixture.

(a) Write the molecular equation describing this reaction.

(b) Write the complete ionic equation describing this reaction.

(c) Write the net ionic equation describing this reaction.

4. When an aqueous $Pb(NO_3)_2$ solution is mixed with an aqueous NaCl solution, a white precipitate of $PbCl_2$ forms in the reaction mixture.

(a) Write the molecular equation describing this reaction.

(b) Write the complete ionic equation describing this reaction.

(c) Write the net ionic equation describing this reaction.

ISBN 0-87540-624-6